The Problem with Preachers:

The Similitude of Preaching, Preying, and Pimping

by Dawud Aasiya-Bey

DORRANCE
PUBLISHING CO
EST. 1920
PITTSBURGH, PENNSYLVANIA 15238

Dorrance Publishing Co
585 Alpha Drive
Suite 103
Pittsburgh, PA 15238
Visit our website at *www.dorrancebookstore.com*

ISBN: 978-1-6461-0621-9
eISBN: 978-1-6461-0101-6

Introduction

The challenge of categorizing preachers with pimps deals with making the connection to what seems to be moral to what is iniquitous. Many preachers operate in authority, supremacy, fame, and impunity over masses of people who are generally victims of misinformation, uninformed consent, tradition, and a susceptibility to suggestion. The role of the preacher should involve directing followers to Christ, away from sin, and disinformation but the status of the position has corrupted the calling. Such compromise emanates from the notion of tithing, innuendos that skate around the word of God, personal and secret lifestyles, promises of blessings linked to money and material gain, manipulation, acquiescing to a lukewarm attitude, and using people to build the personal wealth of the preacher. While considering the platform for the preacher, the overarching design of a societal system in place involves masses yielding to how influential and powerful intellectuals of the past have carefully scripted the fate of the secular world through the use of original sin into commercial systems. This involves the extraction of energy from living, sentient beings or the living soul (you) for committed or omitted wrongdoings. The sin that needs attention is the one that severely impacts the lives of people, which occurs through lacking knowledge in an important area of life. This area of life is simply your status and an incorrect status is where the pimping preacher will have an opportunity to compound the problem by capitalizing on such ignorance. They extract from the very members they purport to help, act as agents of misinformation, fail to empower their followers with the truth, and gain excessively from the energy exuded from many people in a likewise worldly, commercial model.

In order to set the tone for why the preacher can be categorized as a pimp, it is necessary to comprehend the connection of sin in commercial systems and the link to the church platform where the pimping preacher operates. The rest of the pimping behaviors will simply be an extension from this platform. The beginning of the fraud deals with any church that operates under a 501 C 3 document that renders a nonprofit and tax-exempt status with benefits and other stipulations. A church needing this document to operate is something to consider while analyzing the problem with preachers.

The belief that one must pay for the transgressions of an ancestor is another link to the problem even after Jesus Christ asserted that no one pays for the transgressions of an ancestor. The fraud is even more evident when the seventh commandment, "Thou shalt not steal," is being violated on a regular basis. A preacher who steals from church members and uses tricks to do so and shows no conviction while violating this commandment is most assuredly a pimp.

The ability to survive amid the enormity of strict codes, statutes, and ordinances that are encrypted in such a way to elicit confusion is the plight of the living soul. In society, every individual or person is subject to codes because of a status, which is established when one signs documents that attach numbers to the living soul. Those numbers range from birth certificates, social security numbers and driver's license numbers. If the mindset is to operate under the guidelines of these attached numbers in a competent manner, it is virtually impossible to be free. The codes associated with these numbers have an enslaving result even upon the slightest miscomprehension or violation. This is the link to the living, sentient soul being attached to something that is fiction, which is the incorrect status. This status is just one example of where it all begins and permits the system to disenfranchise the individual at the strictest measure of the codes. Those codes resemble strict sets of guidelines and rules that are scripted in the Old Testament and consequences for violations. Moreover, the problem continues when subscribing to documents that indicate the fiction and insidiously tricks one into thinking they are the same as the living soul. The living soul is left to believe that it is the only way to function economically and socially. However, the codes have a freeing aspect for those who recognize that status must be changed to establish some semblance of freedom. It now becomes important to read the United States code, the Roman canons of law, HJR 192, the Administrative Procedures Act and most importantly, the Bible.

And while considering the connection to the Bible, the fulfillment of the law in the New Testament is what exists in the commercial model. Fulfillment deals with waking up and recognizing that even one violation of the law really means that you have violated all. When a preacher insists that followers need to tithe to support a ministry and then goes as far is indicating that they will be cursed with a curse according to scriptures, they are operating under the law and misconstruing the context of scriptures. This fraudulent behavior causes one to give out of necessity while negating the cheerful aspect of giving as indicated in the Bible. Correcting this behavior is something the masses need to consider when giving, by way of an offering rather than succumbing to the games of Federal Reserve notes being seeds for blessings.

Correcting one's status in this commercial system is a step towards freedom even when it seems dauntingly challenging when dealing with the notion that the scripters have had hundreds of years of planning, perfecting, and putting disinformation agents in place to dissuade one from doing so. First, it must be comprehended on what it means to change status. We live in a world of commerce that assigns numbers to virtually everything. Those numbers are linked to living souls in so many facets. There's the social security number, which now connects to driver's license numbers, and there's the birth certificate and marriage license for that matter. By looking at the social security number, we need to ask ourselves, how important is it to have such a number and what is the true purpose of this number? The virtual impossibility of not violating some aspect of the codes related to these numbers make it that much important to change one's status as it is an endless price for remedy. This work is not a step-by-step procedure in how to do this but it is necessary to mention when looking at many church entities that operate under numbers connected to another entity, which can be the state.

Why would the preacher withhold teaching members that changing status is important? Well, either they are unwilling, unable, ignorant, or intentional about taking advantage of the masses. If the preacher is knowledgeable about maintaining their status to manipulate masses of people, then they operate as a pimp. If the preacher finds out later about any fraud and is unwilling to do something about it, then they are a pimp. If the pimp is unable to do something about taking advantage of the masses because it is the tradition of the church to operate this way or it is uncomfortable to do so, then they are a pimp. A ministry operating under the nonprofit document known as the 501.c.3 is just a small example of what is coded in law and imbedded in commercial systems. If churches function under this document, it is subject to what the document says and when the state's code deviates from the biblical principles, all subscribers must yield to its effects and essentially compromise from what is scripted in the Bible. Essentially, by subscribing to a state document, the church that the preacher oversees now has the Bible and the philosophy of the state. So now, if the state said that you must get the social security numbers of all of your members, then the church must do so. If the state indicates that it is okay to have multiple wives, then such philosophy might trickle down to the church, which will have to perform the ceremony and ordain this activity. The latter case is a bit extreme but the point remains that if another entity allows the operation of the church under their guidelines in the commercial system, then they can also set the tone in how those activities occur. If a church is to function with the goal or the vision to do what it is purposed to do, then why have guidelines set in place by another entity such as the state? Churches that operate under a 501c3 are subject to the codes and any deviation can result in being penalized at some point in the violation. So what is really going on? One aspect embodies a tax-exemption status afforded to churches while the members pay taxes and participate in tithing, which is really another tax. In one sense, if the leader of the church teaches the importance of tithing while the ministry that they thrive on is afforded tax-exempt status, then the members should be given the same status. Doing unto others as you would have done unto you should be the case. Another component of the fraud involves the preacher telling you that you are in the world and not of the world but then fail to tell you how to empower yourself by divorcing yourself from the system that disenfranchises you.

In a world of epidemics and pandemics, the latter shows COVID-19 disrupting businesses and the ability to attend the business of church. Preachers have had to close their doors and subscribe to what the state has told them to do even when it seemed unreasonable regarding safety measures. In a normal sense, churches would have congregants sit in the pews or seats and listen to praise and worship and the preacher at some point. However, at the onset of COVID-19, churches had to close their doors because it was not essential to assemble and worship even though it was safe to assemble in hardware stores or sit in a closed airplane tube with recycled air. The same church leaders closed their doors and quickly evolved to online services, collected money virtually, and some received checks from the state for subscribing. The same leaders in church advocated wearing masks and promoted experimental vaccinations, which is not the role of a preacher. The preacher should preach the word of God, not what the world or science promotes. So there is no longer a trust in the divine creator related to healing or a God who protects but that of a pharmaceutical, clinical response that voids any trust in an immune system that was beautifully crafted by the divine creator. A pimp preaches that God is a healer and that no weapon formed against you will prosper but then tells you to get a vaccine, wear a mask, don't think for yourselves or ask questions, continue sending your money, because it is the reward for doing what you were told to do in their ministry.

So the sheep are not at all concerned about what is in infusions that are being promoted by pastors or preachers that will tell them to get a vaccination or wear a mask. It is shameful how preachers subscribe to the perpetuated fear pitched by the mainstream media and yet it should be preached that God has not given us the spirit of fear. They use the church grounds as testing and vaccination centers and subscribe to the idea of persuading members to get tested, wear masks, and get inoculated without any discernment of what is really going on. The madness continues as the preacher uses the church as the stage that emulates the secular world, which gets its instructions from the 16th century events at the Counsel of Trent that impact us today.

The development of original sin at the Counsel of Trent involved the plot on the fate of mankind. The results challenge the inalienable rights of living sentient beings and enables dead entities or corporations to have power over masses of people. This power is made possible by jurisdiction and claim over an individual's profitable interests. Just imagine for one moment that you were able to develop something or create something and another entity told you must yield a portion to them, an entity that you don't even know or even really know why it would have claim on something you did. Did we ever ask ourselves the question, "Why do I owe the IRS a portion of my earnings?" Everyone thinks that they owe some sort of debt, which is based on the principal of original sin. The IRS is just one entity that is involved in such disenfranchisement. The Roman Canons of Law will show original sin and the reader will be able to disseminate its impact and how the corrupt, greedy, controlling leaders at the Counsel of Trent managed to put it all together in a manner that is still in use today with taxation, court systems, and jurisdiction. Original sin is the means for commercial control in societies worldwide and the pimping preacher plays a significant role in ensuring that masses of people yield to its effects. And as many people grapple with the difficulties associated with original sin, this worldwide commitment to pay debts that were created by others is directly linked to paying for the transgressions of an ancestor. The effects are complex as one experiences a lifetime of disenfranchisement of inalienable rights.

Masses of people struggle with the problems associated with original sin, which has the sentiment that we are unworthy because of some former ancestral wrongdoing. It is a lifelong journey of feeling a commitment to pay some type of debt that has been already put into place by the status quo. While the rest of us struggle to make ends meet, the authors of the commercial system relax to the tune of trillions of dollars on the backs of masses of people. The money and greed has led to the ability to integrate more and more codes and hide the truth in such a mirage of confusing codes and laws. Now, the role of preachers involves satiating the minds of many people with messages of hope even in instances where they are aware of fraud but feel helpless or unknowledgeable to do something about it. Preachers then assert a special connection to God, which tricks the masses into thinking that the answers to the corruption will come from the man in the pulpit who references the scriptures that will save people from themselves or eternal damnation. In the process, the preacher will build his ministry empire while controlling the sheep into the mindset that they will one day be blessed if they simply hold on and support the work of the ministry. People are often engaged and heavily distracted by the preacher's ministry. This distraction has people wrapped up in the lifestyles, behaviors, dreams, aspirations, demands, and visions of a preacher. In fact, following and facilitating the vision of a preacher puts the follower in a position that resembles an infant in constant need of validation and nurturing through the approval of a preacher that they yearn to please. The distraction continues as the infant follower never fulfills their dreams and aspirations because they are inundated with the activities of the preacher's ministry. Their dreams are thwarted by an inability to focus on empowering themselves by continuing to operate in an environment of victimization.

Followers of pimping preachers might recognize fraud by directing attention to how Jesus Christ dealt with the corruption in temples where buying and selling took place. Jesus attributed this to a den of thieves and turned the tables as he addressed the corruption that existed in a place of worship. What

Jesus did was a necessary clear message on something that continues to occur in churches to this day. It is so amazing how preachers always assert how the Lord is always telling them something and yet find themselves in a position soliciting people for money and using innuendoes to get the money if the money goal isn't met. The pimping preacher's words have had more precedence over what scriptures say or even those who follow the words of Jesus Christ. If the desire is to embrace what it means to be a Christian, then the words of Jesus Christ should be relevant and not those of a pimping preacher. The problem continues as many of the pimping preachers who will talk of the words of Jesus Christ and then lay claim to the behaviors of many of the Old Testament figures.

When followers of pimps have a fear of God, they experience it from what it is taught. The scriptures assert that "God has not given us the spirit of fear," and yet it can be gauged how this spirit permeates churches throughout the world and enables preachers to maintain control over their followers. For instance, people fear that they won't be in good favor with the preacher if they don't respond to demands or requests. People fear that their finances will be adversely affected if they don't put money in the offering plate. Some fear that they will be cursed with a curse if they do not tithe. Others fear some type of calamity if they say something negative about the preacher even when it reveals truth about what a preacher has done.

Followers work to gain favor of a preacher by trying to live a life that looks like the preacher that they admire. However, this is not possible because many times what is preached from the pulpit is not the life that the preacher lives. The preacher seemingly has success in the areas of marriage, finances, and health but many times, it is a façade. Preachers ask for money to fulfill their visions, some cheat on their wives at conferences and swap wives with the deacons in a lascivious and open-marriage lifestyle. But a church attendee will only see what appears to be the best of the preacher's lifestyle, which is portrayed at a given moment in time as one listens to the preacher. Followers act like children in constant need of a spiritual advisor. This dependency is evident when the members who attend every Sunday get fed the word without taking the time to read the scriptures for themselves. They are more dependent on what the preacher says rather than what is written in the Bible.

Now if the preacher's lifestyle conflicts with what he preaches from the pulpit, loyal members will excuse the behavior by referencing significant figures in the Bible that have fallen, or will attribute the preacher as simply being a man. This is the stage where the follower grapples with their flawed decision to follow someone that appeared to be blameless. The follower makes adjustments to appease their disappointment, which is why so many continue to be abused by preachers over and over again. In the theoretical words of the social psychologist, Leon Festinger, the loyal follower experiences *cognitive dissonance*, where they justify the fault of their leader with the good that he does. The follower simply cannot contend with the idea that their perception of their leader resulted in a deceptive outcome. They must find a way to cope with the notion that they were unable to discern the truth from the beginning. The coping mechanism points to justifying the wrongdoing by expressing how the good outweighs the bad.

A preacher is a pimp when they become a member of a secret society and then are afforded societal privileges which involves selling out. Why is it necessary to be part of something secretive when the Bible has truth for all who will read or hear for that matter? First, such membership is antithetical to God's word and secondly, it supports what the secret organization purports and not the Bible.

Examining the word "God" brings to light much of the corruption that exists with pimping preachers who somehow mimic the behavior of god—not the divine creator that we think of when we hear the word God. The meanings of "God" surprisingly has conflicting definitions and according to the Webster's Collegiate Dictionary, God is derived from the Germanic word Gad, which means the "invoked one." By taking a closer look at the word "Gad" it is interesting how many religions use God as their deity even when such a word has pagan origins. Some will argue that the eternal, divine creator, God that they speak of is denoted with a capital "G," while the pagan gods are denoted with a lowercase "g." Would it be different if the word Satan was written with a capital S or a lowercased s? So it is important to relinquish playing games with capitalizations and deal with the origin of the word. The origin of the word Gad represents one who tortures, torments, pillages, rapes, and injures. This is not the divine creator but something on the scale of insurmountable evil. And judging by the corruption that goes on in the world today, Gad has certainly wreaked havoc on all scales. Over time the word "Gad" evolved to "God" as translations took place and now for those who worship in spirit and truth, the analysis of who or what is being worshipped becomes even more relevant.

By observing the worship of God in scriptures, the use of Gad can be realized. For instance, when noting in the biblical scripture, Isaiah 65:11, Gad was the Syrian-Babylonian god of fortune. The prophet Isaiah described how the worship of Gad became widespread with the Semitic people and spread throughout Greece and Rome. Such worship is seen through Roman mythology and can be seen that Jupiter was the ruler of all gods and worshipped as the god of the rain, thunder, and lightning. This god was the protector of Rome and worshipped in a place called Capitoline Hill, a name that has a similar modern-day western-front familiarity. Next, the influence can also be seen during the Egyptian Gad-Jupiter worship which is further proliferated through the worship of Amon. The worship continues when observing the Greek, triad worship of the gods and goddesses Jupiter, Juno, and Minerva in what symbolizes the Roman cult. The concept of the trinity is based on this historical evidence. So this brief analysis of the connection to Gad to God and it being used as the one to worship in many religions indicates some type of confusion. This uncertainty of God being connected to the true divine creator and being widely used in many religions with different belief systems warrants some concern.

Furthermore, the etymology of the original, early Persian definition of God, which is derived from "Gad," is linked to fortune. If preachers know God based on this definition, then they knowingly participate in this representation. A preacher who purports to be a man of God can be found living a lifestyle of the rich and famous and will justify it with the work that he does. He will go further by using example figures in the Bible who were rich and doing the work of God. And the members of such pimps will back up this silly notion that he is the man of God and will bestow him with gifts and money on a regular basis. The pimping preacher simply has an infatuation for material gain and power over the minds of many. He will use this power to extract at will what he desires in his ministry and will get the membership to help bring it to fruition.

Now if a pimping preacher embraces God in the sense of an eternal divine creator, they might unknowingly and later, knowingly partake in any fraud. And why? Simply because preachers who live a material lifestyle of comfort and greed become relatively comfortable in such lifestyle. If they came to the realization that they were depriving others at the success of their selfish desires, they are unwilling to change or admit such fault. The pimping preachers further experience relative deprivation whereby they are never satisfied with the luxuries that they have and will always want more. This mentality is fueled by his members who look up to him and nurture this inane behavior. It's no wonder that the pimping preacher lives on a platform of greed because he struggles with dealing with his distorted behavior that is fueled by his followers.

The behavior of the preacher who views God as the divine creator needs a closer analysis as subjugating the divine creator's creation is a major contradiction. So how is it possible for one preacher to extract energy from so many if it is purported that we were created in the image of God? Why should a single preacher rule or influence countless people? The pimping preacher is in fact acting as a superhuman and prevents sentient beings from finding within themselves the true divine creator. In fact, the pimping preacher shrouds this opportunity for the living sentient being to communicate with the creator. He takes the energy from his followers through the attention he receives from his members in so many forms. These forms can range from the gifts that are bestowed to him to the energy given to him by the very nature that people have dedicated their thoughts and decisions to the words he says. The preacher in this case is empowered because the attention is directed to him rather than the divine creator. He boldly continues on a higher level than his supporters as observed in churches where the pastor sits and stands on a pulpit that is higher than the members who are forced to look up to him. The energy and attention he receives from his many followers is a form of worship.

The behavior of pimping preachers mirrors the behavior of God throughout the Bible, whether it is a loving God or the God who will punish or destroy. Instances in the Bible that depict God as the destroyer such as "The Great Flood" is indicative of God's wrath in what was eventual destruction to those who ignored the words of the prophet Noah. Under Noah's leadership, the ark was built to save or protect those who would get in at the appointed time. The pimping preacher will use stories like this to control the minds of his members. It is a subtle attack on the members regarding imminent calamity when one does not obey the words of the prophet.

The importance of seeing how God is portrayed in the Bible connects to how most preachers of congregations behave. They mirror or attempt to mirror the behavior of God and the prophets through expressions of the will of God. For instance, when a preacher expresses how God spoke to him about his vision of a new church with a school and business center, this will usually occur upon the obedience of the supporting members. This in itself validates in the minds of the members that the preacher did hear from God when these things come to fruition. On the contrary when things don't go so well such as a leader being found in some type of wrongdoing, the sense of relief or justification comes about when viewing how some leaders in the Bible have fallen or have been subject to scrutiny in their mistakes.

The failure of many preachers in teaching their followers to empower themselves occurs because they exist on a platform where they want all of the attention. They view themselves as the shepherd while the remaining masses play the role as sheep. In fact, it would be against the best interests of the pimping preacher to teach empowerment to his members since it will take away from his recognition and glory. The pimping preacher wants acknowledgement, attention, and royal treatment. He wants to be treated like he is greater than another sentient being. He wants to treat his members like perpetual children. Now on the other hand, some preachers might feel that they do empowered their followers by giving select members access to special treatment and money-making opportunities but the empowerment is much greater than anything tangible that the world can offer outside of anything that the divine creator already promises. The church platform operates similarly to the government bailing out a bank or company when in a financial crisis. Those companies are now under the auspices of the supporting entity. The church can also act to help people in the time of crisis but this alone can create a dependency and a loyalty that can distort the true origin of deliverance.

What is fascinating is that the followers of preachers will not openly admit that their worship is toward the preacher but when observing how they behave toward the preacher; it becomes more apparent that the worship is toward the pimping preacher. The pimping preacher has placed himself on a level that is greater than the masses that support him. He controls the destiny of many people who are brainwashed into thinking that they are not the controllers of their fate. By listening to the words of the preacher and acting on it indicates the preacher's control over another's fate. It might involve something as simple as giving to the ministry or making major decisions with finances, marriage, or family matters.

The followers of these pimps are at fault for not realizing that they are being pimped and if they study the scriptures for themselves, they will know that their support of pimping preachers is outright against the scriptures in the Bible that they should be studying instead of hopping, jumping, shouting, and behaving emotionally in church while the pimp continues to extract resources. People need to wake up and stop acting like children in constant need of a leader. The scriptures in the Bible indicate that a believer should not give authority for someone to govern their lives. This is exactly what a follower of a pimp does. They allow someone who claims to be a servant to govern their lives. A preacher is supposed to be a servant of the people and yet quite the opposite exists. In the same context, the government is supposed to be a service to the people but quite the opposite exists. In the following scripture, *I Samuel 8:4*, the warnings from God to the people of Israel can be mirrored to how the followers of pimps behave. During this time, the people asked for a king to rule over them because they thought this would be a benefit to them. God answered Samuel's prayer by telling him to give the people what they asked for. They have already turned their backs on God and now they want a king to rule over them. He then instructed Samuel to warn them of the consequences of their desire to want a king to rule over them. They would be told of the terrible things that this king would do to them and they simply ignored and rebutted these warnings from Samuel with their desire to have a king whom they thought would fight for them and make their nation like all of the other nations. They simply wanted to be like other nations rather than being what God wanted them to be. Thematically, this scripture illustrates the behavior of those who follow or simply insist on having a pimp rule over them. They will justify the need for a preacher in their lives and will base it on their own belief system despite all of the corruption that exists around them. A brainwashed, bamboozled, zombie, follower of a pimp will reject the truth and embrace the corruption as if were right.

So where did the need for preachers originate? Why are people in need of a spiritual leader? How did we get to a place to elevate a single man on a platform that is greater than another man? The answers have origins that link to leaders who rule the world through a cryptic, perpetual system that insidiously enslaves masses of people with colossal wealth and power results for a select few. This is accomplished by an established and innovative system of control established through violence and fear and imbedded in all levels of society. A preacher simply has a key role in such system that continues to extract energy from unsuspecting women and men.

Making sense of all of this involves an analysis of the driving force where the success of the deception thrives. Amazingly, it is the concept of sin, which is predicated on the Biblical reference that all are born into sin and shaped into iniquity. Original sin, which is a 16th century creation, destines everyone to having to pay or face an eternal grave of suffering by some wrongdoing committed by ancestors. This is the basis for the mind control that begins when it is believed that wrongdoing occurred in the ancestral tree and all descendants must pay for it. People are taught that nothing good dwells in the flesh and sinners have a death sentence that will place them in some eternal place of damnation if not corrected. Now select individuals have created a remedy for the generational sin that will exonerate the sin—through payment, through baptism, communion and a host of other rituals that will grant the individual an opportunity to escape the fate of hell. This fate creates fear and a reliance on leaders or preachers who purport to have the remedy or keep people in check when they attempt to stray away. They assert a special connection to a supreme, eternal God and will use this elitist attitude to control many lives through brainwashing and energy extraction.

The use of sin in society denotes its importance and in its extraordinary simplicity, continues to amass huge economic returns. The system in its design puts pressure on many people through taxation, bank hypothecating, court bench rulings, and a host of millions of statutes with strict controls where people are under so much pressure to behave accordingly to prevent from being fined. The stress created facilitates the need to find solace in some environment, which could be the church. Preachers will use the Bible on this platform to attempt to explain the corruption in the world and they will sometimes appear as heroic in reproving the corruption or those who engage in corruption. They will preach hope, calm fears, and placate the mind through sermons that might attempt to reveal hidden truths in coded messages in scriptures. These hidden messages reveal truth but are left for scholars to try to interpret on meanings that are already known by those who wrote the script.

The preachers who use scriptures to control people to the benefit of their ministries are blatant pimps. They are simply interested in fulfilling their ministry goals, which does not have the best interest of the supporting membership. The brashness of these preachers centers on how God speaks to them about their ministry and how the membership needs to give money and other forms of support to ensure that the vision of the pastor comes to fruition. It then becomes more important to please the pastor, preacher, or man of God rather than a supreme, eternal divine creator. The pastors behave like rock stars with a dying need for attention on a regular basis and feel powerful because people treat them like God. The preachers continue brainwashing people by constantly telling members that they are getting a word from God. In their sermons, they will segue into some story of how God spoke to them as a means to garner the attention and impress the masses of their special connection to God. Would it be interesting if we all heard from God? After being fascinated by the man of God, the followers continue to follow the orders of the preacher—responding to his utterances of the scriptures and yielding to the notion of how money is needed to build his ministry.

The same preacher will persuade his followers to contribute to the purchase of a jet to the tune of several million dollars so that he or she does not have to wait in line at the airport like the rest of the sheep. His excuse deals with spreading the word quickly and efficiently to places that airlines will not conveniently take him. Although there are cell phones in third world countries, the need for private jets might have a hidden agenda that trumps spreading the word to any part of the world.

The followers of these pimps are not taught to empower themselves by learning the truth in society but sometimes fall for the traps that empowerment resolves around being a part of a club or ministry that focuses on acceptance and prospering through material gain. The distraction from the truth encompasses getting the membership to embrace the notion that the preacher is hearing from God and that members are merely there to support. The member is conditioned to believe that they were sent to the ministry by God to support and should not question supporting the preacher or his ministry. And as long as the membership remains asleep and feel that the preacher is the way to God, they will not have the courage, desire, or fortitude to deal with deception.

Individuals are made to believe that a preacher is needed to lead them to the creator and those who come to the church to hear the preacher will come for various reasons like a yearning to make sense of scriptures, dealing with life's problems, getting right with oneself, connecting with the creator, or tradition. They are getting something, however virtual and are willing to pay the price by way of offerings and tithes. Those who are under the leadership of preachers might soon realize that it is all to the benefit of a select few who hold power and information as the truth to everything is reserved for a select few. It is hidden and privileged to those who skillfully continue to hide it. The rest are left to meander through the complexities of a system that is designed to keep individuals thinking that they owe a debt to society.

Recognizing the function of the system helps one realize how pimps easily function in their niche. The system that is being spoken of here is the one that exists in our society and in many modern societies. The system functions through deception and by labeling men as sinners. The deception tells one that slavery has been legislated out of existence when in fact, it continues. It tricks people into thinking that they are free and treats them less than a slave while it operates on lawful slavery. It pretends that you are some worthy citizen while it drains all of your resources and leaves you with the bare necessities to survive. It lies to you so much until you believe the lie to the point that you will label, mistreat, and ultimately fight those who reveal the truth to you. It selects and creates zombies that abuse, intimidate, deceive and control others. It considers anything that a person does within the system as illegal unless they register, license, certificate, and get credentialed. It sticks and prods men and women with substances that will confuse the immune system, which results in disorders at a later time. It forces one to do things against their will. It creates fear and then gets one to respond fearfully to deal with the fear. It secretly labels one as an enemy while pretending one is an ally. It conditions and socializes people to love money and what it does and then limits access to it. It replaces naturally occurring substances with synthesized chemicals in order to fulfill a bottom line. It confuses the population with a sea of statutes which are designed solely to extract energy. These are just a few deceptive instances in the system.

The reason many are deprived at the will of those who hold and conceal information is the idea of perishing for lack of knowledge. If one desires knowledge on the subject of law for instance, then perishing can still exist if the information is difficult to understand, encrypted, and constantly edited to fit the agendas of those in power. Perishing occurs for an inability to decrypt lengthy, verbose, and unclear codes that constantly change. But the system has made it this way. Its design makes it difficult to the point that the individual who tries to decipher might give up and resort to being an accommodating, happy slave. It is evident that think-tank analysis is necessary for interpretation and those who are involved in using the law as a basis to create statutes do so as a means to ultimately deprive rather than preserve a sentient being's rights.

The mindset of control starts from the top and trickles down throughout all levels in society. But it seems that everyone in society has subscribed to a system where a select group of leaders govern as opposed to the other way around. So leaders are allowed to dictate lifestyles and have forgotten the fact that the people are supposed to tell the government what to do in a republic society. But because tyranny has flourished and we are told that we live in a democracy, people have become afraid or dependent on government. The fear can be attributed to observing how many are treated especially when it connects to something as simple as due process. The dependency thrives on an entity that seems to rescue those from some created need. We trust those who deceive us and listen to rhetoric about democracy when aspects of socialism, and even communism to some extent, exists in our nation. The ability to behave like free individuals has been thwarted and we are eternally children with no desire to grow up or behave responsibly for our own thoughts or actions. We have become zombies in a lifestyle of relying on others to think for us.

Many people in society are socialized into looking to others to lead them. An example in the Bible depicts Moses leading the people out of the bondage of slavery in Egypt. This yearning for a leader is based on the notion that they have the best interest of the people they lead. Congressmen, senators, governors, presidents, or preachers that are elected by people rule under the guise that they are on the same level as those whom they rule as it pertains to law. The interesting notion is that such is not the case as it is impossible to have the interest of those whom they rule when leaders operate under different laws over the people they rule. This is in complete disregard to the simple cardinal rule of doing unto others as you would have done unto you. Rulers are privileged to information that benefits them and their families. There are separate laws for them as they have immunity and special access to insider trading information that would otherwise place the average person in jail. They are not subject to the scrutiny of the many statutes that apply to the rest. They purport to do worthy things but operate under different rules. Next, leaders use our trust and beliefs against us. They know that our minds are conditioned to trust them and will make promises of things that they will do while putting us in situations of dependency.

The republic from of government in our society that is so clearly spelled out in Article 4, Section 4 of the United States Constitution and recited daily by students across America is not what is actually practiced in the nation. Currently and since 1929, the government has amassed control of its citizens by creating a reliance resulting from a planned activity such as the Great Depression. Yes, planned activity and without reservation it is difficult to accept that somehow the dollar lost its value in a commercial system that is under control by a select few. When individuals depend on the government for some type of bailout or help when faced with a problem that seemingly cannot be resolved by the individual, then the role of dependence becomes relevant. This example mirrors itself with the church environment that is run by preachers who proclaim to have answers for the societal problems. Again we have allowed the government to tell us what to do instead of the other way around. We allow preachers to tell us what to do instead of the other way around even as many preachers assert that they are humble servants of the Lord, they manage to control many lives without question.

If it can be imagined that it is acceptable to embrace the notion that good things result from bad things, then some might say that it is okay to be corrupt. Some might embrace the workings of evildoers if the end result is something good as it is closure to the wrong that has been done. Others might acquiesce to the notion of permitting evildoers do what they will as they will pay the price in hell. It is the acceptance that there will be evil in the world and the war that goes on is always between good and evil.

Here are several things to consider when dealing with evil in the case of those who revel in deception. It is evil to take advantage of people so that a few can sit on the top and have ultimate power and resources. It is evil to hide information and strategize how to keep it hidden so that many can remain ignorant and never aspire to live as free humans the way the creator designed it. It is evil to hide truth so that people cannot empower themselves in order to really be free. It is evil to harm another human mentally or physically or instill fear in others so that fraud and corruption are maintained. It is evil to wage war and kill countless people to create fear, dependence on government, and creation of war debt that banks finance and then make unsuspecting people pay for it.

In addition to functioning under encrypted codes, leaders continue to take on the attitude of being righteous while violating laws without penalty because of an inherit belief that they can get away with what most do not understand. They are in fact in the company of those who can re-interpret laws to mean something different by simply changing one word in a twisted and loop-holed system. In fact, many leaders continuously break laws they understand or do not understand on a regular basis because the laws that apply to them are different from the laws that apply to the people that they rule over. They go further by harming the rights of every human by behaving as though they are helping people when in fact they are disenfranchising as many as possible of their unalienable rights.

The problem continues as leaders appear to have a perfect slate, that is, they appear to be this ideal model for society. This leads to the reason why so many are shocked when a politician, business leader, or church leader is mixed up in any form of fraud. People who hold power are viewed as the perfect model leader and the reason why many accept the ideas of the leader. This makes it easy for such leaders to have the ability to manipulate masses of people as they pretend that they care while advancing their agendas. And if anyone were to challenge the status quo, their power and influence as gate-keepers, controllers of all means of weaponry, and the training of propaganda agents, will be used to punish, silence, skew, label, and exile anyone who challenges the system. Again, this is a partly why fear exists amongst anyone who might attempt to exercise any knowledge of the law or expose fraud. Many would love to express opposition to any fraud that exists but it is easier to accommodate to protect individual interests and thwart headaches of dealing with any imagined or real repercussions. These dynamics transcend to the church medium where the leaders of ministries behave in the same manner and misinterpret scriptures to control masses of followers.

When fraud exists, it seems that masses of people pay in many ways for the violations of leaders. The payment is not only in money, court fees, or serving a sentence but in an attitude. If a leader is not leading by example, then followers will tend to have the same behavior even if they object to the behavior. It is a mindset that people embrace that if someone at the top misbehaves, it is unreasonable to expect ideal behavior from an ordinary person. This brings us back to the notion that another person is placed on a super-human status. The masses are looking up to one person and expecting them to lead by example and why a need for background checks on leaders are so extensive. People by nature want a perfect model to follow. But this attitude puts leaders above reproach, which is an unrealistic model. No one can truly stand on being perfect in every sense but this ideal model is something that people desire in leadership. Masses are dreaming of this unrealistic model that is ideal and perfect.

A person is born into debt and shaped into paying the debt. The reality, however, is that no debt should have to be paid in a bankrupt corporation but for argument sake, an individual is responsible for paying some type of debt. If the debt isn't paid, be prepared to face some form of punishment which includes and is not limited to imprisonment, eviction, foreclosure, penalties, garnishment, levies, repossessions, fees, taxes, electrocution, inoculation, seizures, child support, spousal support, alimony, and a host of other means of punishment. Rulers have amassed control through these forms of violence, mind-control, manipulation, and a host of other trickery in order to maintain power. They have people in position in order to maintain control and have had plenty of time to set up a diverse and encrypted system that needs much skill to understand. People live in fear and unnecessary stress due to all the factors that are set in place to monetize on sin and it does not always result in physical violence. In reality, it is physical violence because the mental violence that people experience on a regular basis leads to physical stress on the human body. In essence, because of the mental stress that exists, it is realized that hypertension, psychological disorders, and cardiovascular disease is linked to mental stress. So although a gun or a bomb might not have been used, slow destruction of the human body is facilitated by the continuous stress.

The constant exposure and fostering of the worship of money, materials, actors, pop stars, athletes, and politicians through media forms has origins that date back to antiquity as shown in scriptures and archeological findings. The Bible shows countless examples of the worship of materials. The golden calf and the description of the riches that Solomon possessed, and streets being paved in gold in a heavenly description are just a few examples. Imagine streets being paved in gold which might be indicative of gold's unimportance but what remains is that gold has been a standard for something of importance and value. That value has been commandeered by a select group of people who control everything. We are not in control of our destinies and we follow what the gatekeepers tell us and how the chess masters dictate the future. Gold was once the standard but now society operates on something totally different which has made humans the standard to where energy can be extracted in the form of some twisted, diabolical, form of slavery that has calcified the masses of people to its existence.

The masses of people have not laid up treasure on the earth but a small segment of people have done so by controlling virtually everything or at least the perception that they do. This alone does not constitute what is evident and current in our society as the worship of things pervades our existence. We are linked to belief systems that emanate from the worship of things. And although many claim to worship the divine, material things seem to have precedence over the divine. It is extreme and ubiquitously saturated in our culture in media forms and not uncommon to witness many having extreme emotion in the presence of such idols.

The worship of materials and the desire for fame and fortune is a societal pressure as people feel the need to be like someone portrayed in a movie, a book, magazine, Internet, or simply their neighbor. A person might aspire to be successful through material gain or being in the company of people whom others adore. The stage is set as the media, stadiums, courts, churches, and other platforms facilitate the process of aggrandizing all of these things to such insane idolatry levels.

In another instance, there are select individuals in society that receive favors, relief, immunity, or simply get exonerated in the face of wrongdoing. In essence, they behave as though they are above the law. In reality, they are not above the law (perhaps the laws or codes that they have made) or reproach but this benefit has been bestowed to them. The larger problem exists at the top and filters down as rulers treat members of its corporations like lifetime children that simply never grow up to function as adults. In this sense, it is "do what I say and not what I do."

People seek relief in churches or similar venue in order to connect with the divine, escape from the vicissitudes of life or make sense of a failing life status. This process is facilitated by the notion that society has already created the needs and already benefits by profiting on one's sin through breaches in contracts to violent crimes. It is the means to extract money from individuals. So the church operates similarly and those who enter the church are taught that they are sinners that can now be helped. This humbles the individual in the midst of those who purport to be righteous and will pay a price while aspiring to be righteous. The believer will in fact pay offerings and tithes to ministries that claim to do good for the individual and the community.

Many people are being controlled because of an inherent belief that preachers have good intentions. People give to a particular ministry, which results in some type of success and credited toward the preacher. Such leader is looked upon with great admiration and respect but the sad reality rests with how the leader might view his supporters, which in many cases is on a lower level than himself. Some will argue that they do not feel this way but when you observe the behavior of many preachers, you will be assured that the preacher views himself on a higher plain. He views his supporters like children and will manipulate and use them solely for his benefit. He behaves like he is all-knowing, which is fueled by the fact that he is the center of decisions in church and family matters. In this perception, he is the one who has answers to the world's problems.

There is no distinction between the pimp and preacher as both manage to manipulate, lie, and take from those who trust them. Those who assert that false preachers are wolves in sheep's clothing actually support the notion that false preachers are pimps, which leads to addressing these questions. What qualifies a preacher as a pimp? Is the role of a preacher designed to control the masses? How do pimping preachers continue to succeed in deceiving people even when it is learned that they have done something wrong? Is the inspiration to becoming a preacher similar to the mindset of wanting to become a pimp? Are preachers living up to the role that they purport? Understanding how imposter preachers insidiously and overtly fit the description of pimp first requires an assessment of the characteristics and business of the pimp and his prostitutes. It will then be determined how this parallels with the preacher and his followers.

The Oxford Dictionary defines pimp as "a man who controls prostitutes and arranges clients for them, taking part in their earnings in return."[2] This concise definition is expanded by exploring the immoral nature of the pimp who enjoys a flashy lifestyle of expensive clothing, jewelry, vehicles, and homes at the auspices of his prostitutes. The pimp's narcissistic disorder is fueled by self-indulgence and a propensity toward self-aggrandizement. He substantiates his delusion of importance by surrounding himself with expensive material possessions with a deficiency in sophistication even as he attempts to behave like a boulevardier. The pimp's motive is to capitalize on any opportunity to control prostitutes for a monetary benefit with a distorted business ethic that takes the majority of the prostitute's earnings.

It is estimated that pimps control fifty percent of the prostitution that exists in our society. The National Center for Missing and Exploited Children[1] estimates that 1 in 5 girls and 1 in 10 boys are sexually abused or assaulted before they reach adulthood. The pimp is at the center of these statistics as he benefits by recruiting potential vulnerable victims by visiting malls, bus and train stations, neighborhoods, arcades, and college and university campuses. These are opportunities for the pimp to establish relationships with potential clients. He is sly and cunning and does not appear to be the stereotypical pimp who wears flashy garments but looks like the ordinary person who will simply garner the attention of those who are in need. Pimps work on capitalizing on the needs of individuals and they use this as the means to take advantage of people.

There are many factors that allow the pimp to profit in a business of getting money from prostitutes. First, he acts like the protector to the prostitute but lacks the ability to do so even in the scenario of hiding in a closet as danger exists every time a prostitute participates in an act deemed to yield a profit. The risky behavior associated with prostitution usually results in disease, psychological disorders, drug addictions, incarceration, and abuse.

As far as pimping preachers go, they use the church, which is typically like the bank and the church needs members in order to function under the 501C3 nonprofit status. Members have the mindset that this is a place where they can receive help. Does this sound familiar? People go to the bank to start an account or to get a loan. Banks make people feel like they need the bank in many respects without really letting people know that the bank needs people. For instance, if a person comes to the bank for a loan, they will check your credit and see if you did something wrong. They will use your wrongdoing as a means to charge higher interest rates and penalties. They will label you as though you are some bad person and tell you that you have to pay for your bad credit. However, they are using your credit to hypothecate or do their fractional reserve banking on your signature. But you spend months or years paying interest and penalties while the bank has immediately benefited by you setting up an account. They won't tell you this but would rather operate in corruption so they could essentially steal from you.

The preacher acts like the banker as he knows that you have come to the church as a sinner. He will tell you that salvation is free but you will then feel inclined to support such ministry because you've yielded yourself to man who appeared to be the link to your forgiveness. When the preacher solicits help from the membership to support his ministry, you will think back on that special moment when the preacher ushered you in to getting forgiveness for your sins and becoming part of a ministry that will help you stay on track. It is realized that members will ultimately give something to continue the advancement of the mission of the pimp.

When looking at another societal example such as how courtrooms function, it can be noted that the dynamics are essentially the same. People enter the courtroom with a degree of fear for a crime that they might have committed or are led to believe that they have committed. They enter the courtroom with fear with hopes that an attorney will plead their case in a way that prevents them from having to pay a fine or go to jail. The potential member enters the church with a similar fear as they enter with the label of a sinner that needs God to forgive them if they don't want to face an eternal damnation or if they expect to make it to a place called heaven.

People enter the church with the belief that they are a wretched individual and in the process will accept the savior to be remised of sins. In the process, this wretched state has a psychological impact on individuals who feel that this is the place where they found Jesus and will be the cheerful giver. After years and years of commitment with giving, the drained giver is now brainwashed by scriptures from the Old Testament promises that a curse will be upon them for not giving. This deception is amazing and continues to permeate from so many church pulpits on any given Sunday.

If Jesus Christ were here today, what do you think he would say to the mega preachers who are living superfluous lifestyles at the notion of the preached word and on the backs of many supporters? In addition to the lifestyle, preachers have the arrogance of celebrity status which is another indication of the corruption. No one should be looking at another human being as greater than another human being as all men are created equal, at least according to what Thomas Jefferson scripted in the Declaration of Independence. But these preachers are living like celebrities and they welcome the attention without pause. Mega churches are in the business to profit and the members make it possible by supporting the fact that preachers need to be wined and dined because they believe if they are nice to the man or woman of God, that they will somehow be blessed. This illogical ideology states that a person needs another person in order to get to the Divine creator. The creator expects us to communicate with him and have a personal link with him without putting trust in another's flesh. If a person is not preaching the words of Jesus Christ, why would they indicate that they are a Christian preacher? These preachers are not preaching the words of Christ or they might be selective about saying what Christ said. Preaching the words of Jesus Christ is all Christian preachers need to do and yet many of the sermons are filled with philosophical jargon and misinterpreted scriptures that have nothing to do with what Jesus Christ was preaching about. In fact, the theme of many sermons centers on building up ministries.

The role of the prostitute is the connection to the pimp's success in his business. Her background originates from one or a combination of environments that deals with sexual abuse at an early age, drugs, domestic violence, poverty, ignorance, and a lack of parental and community support. She views the pimp as a way out of an existing hopeless lifestyle and enters the pimp's world of deception where he pretends to rescue her. He impresses her with an outward appearance of success and then goes further by pretending he has genuine love for her. He then becomes the agent in the scheme of using her body for income and continues brainwashing her into thinking that she benefits when giving him money. This process is made easy by her conditioned mind since the pimp uses her past lifestyle as momentum to control and get her to depend on him. He knows that he can get her to use her body with different individuals while putting aside any feelings of violation, remorse or conviction and will go as far as controlling her thinking through controlled substances.

Prostitution involves sex with many people and usually results in the spread of some type of communicable disease. Based on this factor alone, the pimp is unable to offer protection. The frightening notion is that there isn't enough data to support the prevalence of the spread of disease amongst prostitution because it is viewed as a crime in most places and most people involved in this business are not apt to give data about whether they are using condoms or being involved in prostitution. And when looking at the disease aspect, some might have the attitude that disease can be cured but in the case in the case of HIV or other viral infections, where there is no admitted known cure, some may view it as never happening to them. Those who unknowingly have the disease will infect others in the process. Some who have knowledge of their infection might take it to the level of seeking vengeance on someone simply because someone gave it to them, which is indicative of the many levels of corruption. So it is reasonable to say that the pimp recklessly makes money with no moral concern because the world of prostitution involves injury, disease, death, broken relationships and marriages, psychological disorders, incarceration, pain, misery, and strife, just to name a few. His focus is about getting money from his prostitutes so he can partake in a covetous and material acquiring lifestyle with the attitude of rendering some form of pimp-slapping at the hand of any opposing views.

The vulnerability of a potential prostitute impinges on how she approaches her dream to a better way of life and her behavior is similar to a woman who uses sex to get something out of a man in a rat-race society. The woman, who tries to get ahead in a rat-race world without admission, finds herself behaving in the same manner without actually admitting that she is prostituting. In a more subtle sense, she embraces the sugar daddy who will rescue her in the time of financial or similar needs with an exchange of sex for payment of bills. She is the single parent who feels rejected by her baby's father who is running the streets and not living up to his responsibilities. She will seek a man who she has profiled as being a decent person by the mere fact that he has a job and probably some money that he can share. While both may receive some type of stimulation, the man can be viewed as being pimped because he now has to pay the woman in order to guarantee or secure future pleasures. In another sense, the means to climb the corporate ladder is connected to a compromise that uses sex as the tool. The woman can be viewed as behaving like a pimp in the manner that she benefits when a man does something for her after receiving sex. His mindset is to do something for her so that he can secure future opportunities of sex. He wants to her to feel obligated or guilty so that she will yield to him when he wants sex but the end result is the woman receiving something for the act. So who is the pimp in this scenario?

In the case of the prostitute, a woman succumbs to the pimp who insidiously gives her a false sense of hope and an opportunity to make money with clients that he says he trusts. She feels that this will give her the means to save some money, get citizenship, or get out of the game if of course that is her desire or ability. Unfortunately, the reality is an environment of drugs, drama, jail, and potential disease. It is a game that usually lands women in jail, the hospital, a psychiatric ward or a casket. The outlook of a better way of life using this approach centers on illogic and a distorted fantasy in the final analysis.

The word pimp is derogatory in every sense and its connection with the word preacher becomes less oxymoronic when noting that the pimping preacher is not a preacher but a pimp who attempts to preach the word of God. He possesses the attributes of a pimp and hides under the covering as a preacher. He works in the church with an agenda which appears like he is doing the work of the Lord but his motive is all about getting money. It starts with different strategies that he uses to get potential members and members to grow his ministry. He profiles individuals that he knows will be trustworthy and loyal and who will embrace his distorted vision, which is taking money from people. In his view, these members must be the type that will yield to his whim and acquiesce even when matters cause members to disagree, which is a form of pimp slapping. As potential members enter the church, they will end up having to fill out information cards in order to build his membership. Once he accomplishes this step, he will continue profiling by getting information such as the profession of the individual, family makeup and lifestyle.

The following responses to these questions lead to the true mindset of the individual who desires becoming a preacher and is inextricably connected to wanting to be a pimping preacher. Some things aspiring pastors might say as reasons they want to enter the ministry are: I want to be a servant for people. It's my time or my season. I am ready to start my ministry. I started this ministry in my basement or home. I want to preach because preachers are in my family and I want to keep the tradition going. I want to help others. The Lord spoke to me in a dream and told me to preach the gospel. I want to influence many people. I am great at public speaking. I want to use my psychology background and knowledge of the Bible to help others. People always gravitate to me and tell me their problems and I believe that I can help many through the word of God. The world is lost and I have to do my part in getting more souls to heaven. The Lord healed me and I promised him that I would preach the gospel.

When observing how preachers speak of themselves and their ministries, they have an agenda to empower themselves. They do this by getting others to support some vision and they use God to validate the vision. It is a form of mind control because when you connect something to God, people will entrust you more. They will have buy-in to what you're trying to do because people want browning points from God for doing work on this earth. In the process people get the browning points from the preacher who proclaims that they are connected to God. People believe that these pimps are interceding with God on a regular basis and if they get on the good side of the preacher, the preacher will pray for them and secure their spot in heaven.

When a preacher says that he wants to be a servant to the people, he is basically giving one of the most significant responses to getting ordained in a ministry. He behaves like he is like Jesus Christ but will do otherwise when he gets into the ministry he supposedly serves.

The desire to help others really centers on many people helping the pimping preacher. He will benefit by the masses of individuals sowing into his ministry but then he will appear to be helping others with other people's money. He will be on a platform where he orchestrates the good that the ministry does when in fact he is the beneficiary in many ways.

The desire to want to influence many people is a pimping dynamic that is not connected to doing ministry. A person who has this mindset is not in ministry to do the work of God but has an arrogant desire to control people and to be seen of others.

The pimping preacher gives attention to the members whom he feels will be loyal and will assign them roles that makes them feel as though they are a significant force in the ministry. It is his desire to ultimately get a constant influx of money from church members who succumb to the lies and misinterpretation of scriptures on a regular basis. A favorite and most misinterpreted scripture in the book of Malachi is used to invoke feelings of guilt for those who do not give. It is not uncommon to hear from the pulpit, "Will a man rob God?" or this notion of being cursed with a curse for not giving. Pimps instill guilt and use principles of planting seeds to get people to give money. They refer to the seed as money and it fits right in with the misinterpretation that manipulates people to give. The dependence and ignorance of the church members is the means that enable the pimping preacher to continue on his campaign to get money. He relies on the notion that most of the members will not research and study the word for themselves and the ones that do and who are privy to his foolishness will eventually get ousted from the pimp's ministry or simply leave out of frustration.

Pimping preachers do not care about the teachings in the Bible. Some have simply looked at the opportunity to make money and have watched pastors over the years successfully do this. They embrace the style of some of their favorites over the years and will mimic their behaviors. They want all of the recognition in the things that are made possible by the membership. They will use the scriptures that apply to how the preacher benefits. They outwardly display it in their behaviors and the manner in which they flaunt acquisitions that were made possible by the church members who give in the form of tithes, offerings, and personal gifts.

There is a cover-up to the corruption that involves getting money from church members. It involves ministries that do noble things for the community, such as feeding the hungry, providing shelter to the homeless, offering community service and jobs. This creates a covering that enables pimping preachers to thrive unnoticed. They rely on the good that the ministry does while they continue in their immoral behavior. This immoral behavior includes giving false information to the members about expenditures, having sex with the secretaries, sodomizing boys, using money for personal expenses, and ultimately using a nonprofit status to profit from masses of people.

Pimping preachers enjoy the lifestyle that affords them the opportunity to have power over people. They know that they can get people to give money because people generally respect preachers and believe that they are sincere. Pimping preachers do not care that they are stealing the people's money on a regular basis. They view themselves as pillars in the community and feel that they deserve the money and the recognition that people give them. These pimps do not care about parishioners and will treat them like second-class citizens. They feel that they are above the members of the congregation that supports them and will put on the fake smile and treat them as though they are important when they are only concerned about getting money. They do not believe in what they preach because if they did, they would be convicted in the wrongdoing and would realize the consequences for their sin. The pimp is a calculating, premeditating liar and if you are in attendance at one of these ministries, simply look for the signs that might place your pastor in the pimping category. Moreover, it is important to wake up and study the scriptures for yourself.

The persona of the pimping preacher puts him at the center of attention and he gets this by manipulating church members to praise him and treat him as if he is some special anointed figure that is connected to God. He gets attention by wearing expensive clothing and influencing women and men with an outward appearance of success. He uses Aramaic, Greek, and Hebrew interpretations of scriptures to act as though he is really connected to the meaning of ancient texts. The pimping preacher is not called into ministry by God but is motivated by a selfish desire to take advantage of the uninformed churchgoers who are victimized on a regular basis by the many strategies and tactics often used by the creative pimp. Again, he profits on a nonprofit status and conducts his business on a platform, which makes him seem like a legitimate person of the cloth.

The pimping preacher's victims range from members from all walks of life. Such members go to church based on some traditional value and must find themselves in a house of worship on a Sunday morning. The mindset might be that their parents and grandparents always went to church on Sunday and it would not seem right if not in attendance on a Sunday. They will use scriptures like "forsake not the assembling of the righteous" to validate this belief. Some will attend church because they simply need a way out of an existing volatile and hostile environment at home. Situations of domestic violence give the church attendee an opportunity for hope by going to a place that might offer help. Some women might go to church to address unmet needs by their significant other. These victims go to church to try to get something from an environment that offers hope through the preached word of God. The victim's intent might be to get something in a world of quid pro quo, which mostly benefits the preacher. Members or potential members are willing to pay money for someone who speaks to their condition. In fact, it is like visiting a psychologist or psychiatrist for that matter and many of these pimps are skilled in dealing with issues related to the mind. People from all walks of life have emotional, financial, physical, and spiritual needs and can easily rely on the preacher to speak to those conditions. These inescapable dynamics of the human condition are addressed by the pimping preacher and establish the momentum that helps him get the support he needs.

There is an opportunity cost that has been considered by the pimp as he decides to do ministry as a pimp. He realizes that the benefits outweigh the costs and will accept his calling as a pimp rather than work a regular job that might have benefits. He forgoes the cost working a job that offers a fixed income and possible dental and medical benefits to working in ministry, which offers much more. He no longer has to punch a clock or answer to anyone. He gets fringe benefits from the members who treat him as if he is the head-of-state. This is validated by the idea that some pastors refer to their wives as the first lady. So much attention and focus is on the clergy rather than the word. He desires to live a lifestyle of a rich person and this is done by a continuous influx of money by the members. It can be looked at as a virtual product that he offers every Sunday. He sells the word and members are willing to pay for it. He gets people to say amen to his foolishness on a regular basis.

The pimping preacher is skilled at the art of manipulation and preys on single women who look at him like a father, husband, or mentor figure. He gets their loyalty by preaching to their condition and will even use resources to help the single woman. Such women feel indebted to the preacher and will promise to give on a regular basis or they will ultimately give when they are able. This deceptive plan controls vulnerable women who are some of the biggest supporters of such pimping regimes.

Pimping preachers have women under their control in the same manner that a pimp controls women. He is afforded the opportunity on a weekly basis to speak to their conditions and uses the Bible to garner their trust while he addresses their issues. The important realization is that a vulnerable woman is drawn in by a man who wears a suit, drives a fancy car and who appears to have some form of intellect. Many of these women find refuge in a church where the pimp will have an opportunity to control their lives and way of thinking from the pulpit, which transcends to the home-front of the individual. The pimping preacher starts off by using scripture to control women and creates a scenario that makes the woman equally yoked with him when she should be aligning herself with her husband. This is the reason why some ministries are instrumental in increasing the divorce rate. The pimping preacher gets the individuals to live by his philosophy while discounting their spouses. It is a compromise that is the fuel to the many divorces that occur in the church environment. The pimping preacher takes it one step further and dissuades such women from her involvement with a man that is not in attendance at his ministry and uses the unequally yoked argument to validate such reasoning.

The pimp wants to have ultimate control over a woman's life because he knows that outside influences will negatively impact the single woman's loyalty to the ministry. It is important to realize the higher percentage of women that are in attendance on a given Sunday. Now if a woman plans to marry, the pimp will not support the couple's desire to get married even though the scriptures say that it is better to marry than to burn. He will find fault in such relationship and recommend waiting while he counsels with the intent of getting information. He will then use this information against the couple by discouraging them from getting married or will go as far as using the pulpit to make an example of the couple. In his insidious plot, he will generalize by saying, "this couple" came into my office and shared with me that they were "shacking." This process gives the listening members the opportunity to speculate and thus create an environment of rumors and gossip. The pimp is not at all concerned about the couple entering into an institution designed by God but rather in finding fault so that the woman will remain single and at the whim of the pimping preacher. He will go as far as using the pulpit to illustrate the couple's condition to advance his destructive tactics. Now if the preacher supports the marriage, he will do so with the knowledge that the husband supports the ministry. Again, the pimp wants loyalty from every front and has a major problem with anyone who might challenge such loyalty.

Now the term pimp has another meaning, which discounts the immoral and focuses on the flashy part. This is why it is easy for people to embrace this term in an appealing sense. When one pimps a car, home, or webpage, they are flashing up something that is dull or ordinary. This definition really illustrates how pimps are flashy with their gain. They appear to have material gain by displaying it through the purchase of utterly tasteless and ridiculously flashy garments, jewelry, and cars. This indicates the foolish mindset of the pimp and the idea of pimping is made fun and acceptable in this view. However, this deception does not negate its true meaning and it mirrors the preacher who behaves in the same manner. He possesses these attributes as he takes from church members to fulfill greedy desires. His rich lifestyle of money and material possessions is obtained from church members who are mostly working-class people on fixed incomes.

Some pimping preachers invest in other business ventures that are not connected to the church as a means to dispute those who question their material gain. These pimps behave as if the start-up money for such ventures came from business loans or grants but in actuality, the church members are like venture capitalists or investors that invest in the pimp and facilitate the building of his empire. The unfortunate outcome is that church members will not receive a return on their investments and the deception continues when the members are told that their reward is in heaven while the preacher benefits right now.

Pimping preachers have a proven successful business model that has launched mega ministries. They get talented people from various professions who will be part of a team or advisement committee. During their meetings, they strategize on how to increase membership and what percentage will be used for staff while using the other percentage to build the platform. It then becomes a competition in the world of pimping mega ministries because these pimps look at the demographics and areas where they will build their churches. They want to see how what they offer will outsell the neighboring ministries.

They are a business and will work off a capitalistic model of competition. They will offer childcare, onsite schools, and other conveniences that garner the attention of people. These appealing characteristics draw people who need time to sit in service without having to worry about distractions such as crying babies. It sets the tone for a family-oriented environment as the real agenda is about your wallet and how you will support a ministry that does this.

The competition continues as clergy members concern themselves about who is stealing members as if people should not have the freedom to choose where they would desire attending. These pimps look at members as dollar signs and could care less about who is walking upright. They will adjust their sermons so that they don't offend the biggest supporters of the church. They will use technology to see who is tithing and who is consistently giving on a regular basis. The pimping preacher needs people in order to have a successful pimping dynasty. He cleverly uses the word of God to lure the unsuspecting persons who will help build his success and in the process makes certain the music ministry is in place as it draws people to the ministry. The music elicits the emotions of people and draws them to what appears to be beautiful, ecumenical, and Godly, which sets the stage for the preacher to follow with the word of God. People are tranquilized by the music and then the pimping preacher misuses the word of God against people who aren't studying the word for themselves.

These pimping preachers will give benefits to the parishioners who give the most in the ministry so that they will continue giving to the pimp's regime. They are made to feel important and part of something genuine. They are appointed as deacons, board members, associate ministers (associate pimps), head of security, and other lucrative-sounding positions. As long as these individuals go along with the tides by continuing to tithe and are agreeable in church matters that are influenced by the pimp, they are guaranteed the reserved parking space, keys to access points of the church, security codes, an office, and opportunities to speak in the pulpit. These tactics make them feel important and establishes their loyalty as long-term members. They will become part of a regime that insidiously gets money out of the members on a regular basis. They are in essence the covering for the pimp and will be a shield to him when controversy arises.

The pimping preacher continues to enhance his regime by obtaining information about members who work as professionals in the private sector and uses their skills to enhance running his pimping dynasty. He will garner the skills of CPAs, attorneys, doctors, educators, musicians, human resource experts, police officers, and CEOs of various companies. He will not only admonish them to tithe but will appoint them as church leaders while realizing that their skills can be applied to enhancing the ministry. His motive is to set a multiplier effect in motion from leaders to get others to tithe.

The pimping preacher's ministry succeeds on perpetuity as there is a constant influx of money that makes it to the offering plate on a weekly basis. If the pimping preacher has enough business sense to use the money in a way that will cover expenses even when the membership's giving declines, he will be able to continue growing his ministry. If, however, there is overspending in the ministry, it will be noted that there will be multiple offerings and further tactics to get people to give like campaigns, special services, and concerts to raise money. These services are not designed to meet the individual's needs but they are set up to get money out of the membership.

Some pimping preachers enter the ministry with a humble approach because they are still learning the ropes on how to pimp. When the pimp becomes accustomed to the way things work, they will behave arrogantly. When members complain, he will get in the pulpit and make bold statements that others will replace you or they will go as far as saying that they don't want you in their ministry. The pimp wants loyalty and if doesn't get it, will use measures to get rid of the disloyal individual. It is important to note that the pimp needs loyalty in order to continue advancing his ministry.

The interesting notion is that there is a price tag on the word of God and people are willing to pay to hear someone preach the word. They are lured into believing that they need to give to a ministry that is doing the work of the Lord and the pimp will have many things in place to facilitate the process of giving.

The word is a commodity and if Jesus walked this earth today, he would have to turn the tables again. But since Jesus isn't turning any tables, let's take a look at how the pimp might respond when challenged on material gain. Usually the pimp will boast about business ventures like books, DVDs, and real estate investments outside of the ministry rather than making the claim that many of those ventures became a reality at the backing of other people's money—specifically, church members. These pimps also fail to indicate that they are getting benefits beyond what the normal person gets. They benefit from the money of parishioners, tax exemptions, gas and housing allowances, travel expenses, private jets, planes or helicopters, body guards, and a host of other benefits. The pimping preacher appears important because of all of this and seems like a legitimate man of the cloth. Again, a pimp is scandalous and uses women to do immoral acts so that he can benefit from their earnings with a flamboyant lifestyle. In the same light, the pimping preacher uses the money from the church members to live a superfluous lifestyle.

Now the church has become the stage where people get used and everyone should be sick and tired of all of the pimping and bamboozling that is occurring on a regular basis in many churches in our society. When Jesus preached the gospel, he simply went out and preached and healed those who were sick, lost, confused, and even dead for that matter. He didn't ask for money, appreciation services, fundraising ceremonies, multiple offerings, and false promises of being blessed if you gave money to a particular ministry. It is sad that people fall for these lies but people tend to trust a minister or preacher who claims to be a proponent of the word of God. The reality is that people should study the word for themselves and be keen to the wolves that are in sheep's clothing who are out to get money.

Pimping preachers know that the church is the stage for entertainment purposes. They know that people find comfort in the sugar-coated gospels that will put one in the mindset to support and give to a ministry. A sugar-coated gospel is a message that feels good to people. It is basically what people want to hear and does not focus on rebuking the wrongdoer. It satiates the mind that one will be blessed if they reach into their wallets or purses and give. It makes people believe that good works might get them into heaven. People like to hear that if they plant a seed, they will get blessed but the members of the church should simply go to the store and buy some seeds and start a garden. The blessing will simply be the harvest when those plants yield fruits or vegetables. But these are the methods used to get your money or your talents. If one tells you something that sounds provocative and deep and it speaks to your condition, you might be inclined to give because the ministry or the pimp running the ministry has your interest at heart. Sadly, you are simply a candidate for being pimped and that is the bottom line! In this process, you are willing to allow someone to pimp you out of money. Yes, you will pay money on a weekly basis so that the choirs, praise teams, and preachers can entertain you and the pimp experts can make promises that they cannot keep. I once heard a pastor admonish people to give and then he said, "I promise that you will get a blessing from your giving." How can a pastor make such a claim? He then said in his next sentence, "If you don't get blessed, we will refund your money." First of all, what is meant by "we will refund your money"? Is this pastor trying to trick people into thinking that it is the leadership in ministry that is behind the coercion for everyone to give rather than a single pastor or preacher? Is it a ploy to get people to think that it is a ministry that is asking for money and not the pastor because people need to have buy-in to giving? People will tend to give to a ministry that claims to help the poor and are less likely to give to a minister who solely invites people to give because pastors living large on other people's money is not unfamiliar. Further, the use of the pronoun "we" offsets the idea that an individual is trying to get the money but it really amounts to a collection of pimps. How can a pastor make a promise that you are going to get blessed and then in the very next sentence say that they will refund you if you do not get blessed? So, in essence, this pastor didn't really believe what he was saying and needed to reassure you of your blessing by promising your money back. In fact, this pastor doesn't believe that God is going to do any blessing because he would not have made such an offer of just in case God didn't come through, you would get your money back. He should have said, "I'm not sure if God is going to bless you if you give but give anyway and if it causes a financial hardship, we will refund your money." Furthermore, what type of blessing is this pastor talking about? Will the giver get a ROI (return on investment)? Will the money come back one hundred fold? Will the person be cured of an incurable disease? Please tell me what type of blessing is taking place. Now in his disclosure, this pastor will refund people who do not get blessed from their giving? So the faith thing is out the door and the promise is based on something man will do, because he did not really believe that God would bless the giver. Now what would happen if the person decided to go back and get a refund because they didn't get this blessing the pastor was talking about? This blessing still remains unknown but some will boldly say something like someone is going to give you a new car or that loan that you applied for is going to get approved. But this pastor might respond to this with more innuendos and tricks. In this scenario, the person would say, "You know, I gave a thousand dollars last week and I didn't get blessed. Can I have my money back?" The pastor's response might sound something like this. "Well, do you have your health and strength? Are you in your right mind? Did he put clothes on your back? Did you give God a chance to work the blessing in your life? Well, you are blessed, so get out of my office acting like some defeated Christian!" Pimping pastors will use the Bible as the basis to all of the tricks and artistry against the members in their congregations. These pimping pastors know how to use the word against believers and for their benefit. They know people yield to what the word says especially if they know that the average person is limited in their knowledge of the word. The pimping preacher feels that they can use it to get something out of people and will always fall back on some scripture that sounds deep to trick people into believing what they are saying.

It is estimated that of the approximate eighty thousand churches in the United States, there are twenty percent in attendance on a given weekend[1]. This translates to about seventy-two million people attending church in the United States alone. Now there might be some debate as to the exact number, perhaps more or less but it remains that church attendance has importance in our society. So now the interesting question is, why do people attend church? What does a person gain by attending church? Has the role of the church shifted from helping people to simply helping a person or a ministry? Who benefits most in these ministries? How is it possible that a single person or ministry can take advantage of so many people? These important questions need to be addressed so that there is a better understanding of how some preachers end up being classified in the same light as the pimps and how the congregation might have the same dependent mentality as the prostitutes.

Much can be learned from the dynamics of ministry and this fictional story is just of one of many accounts of what happens in ministries. It my perspective of what goes on in ministries coupled with embellishment by a little creativity of the imagination. In fact, there are many perspectives out there and people have already and will continue to share their stories of the fraudulent activities in ministries. Sadly, many people will stray away from ministries when they are hurt and either stop participating in ministry or simply find another ministry where it seems that things are less volatile. Hopefully, this will heighten your awareness to some of the dynamics in church and prevent you from simply overlooking the corruption. It might motivate one to confront problems instead of sitting back and letting it happen, or humbly walking away. Moreover, it is acceptable to address issues instead of saying, "God is going to deal with those corrupt people." The paradigm shift is simple. Confront the issues and stop acting like we should wait for God to deal with the corruption when God might be leading us to do something about it.

Now, the challenge labeling a preacher as a pimp deals with the preachers using scriptures to validate their lustful, lascivious, greedy, and covetous behavior. If one does not have an understanding of the scriptures, it might sound as though the pimping preacher does not fit the category of pimp. But it is necessary to study and be keen to the tricks so that pimps do not take advantage of people. The sincere preacher will have the heart that will not allow temptations or selfish agendas to get in the way.

The pimps in the pulpit do not believe in what they are preaching and they realize that people can study the word for themselves by using by the library, Internet, book store or universities for information. A pimping preacher will use scriptures and even listen to sermons on TV, Internet or radio as part preparing for their sermons. They will adjust it slightly and have people thinking that they are on one accord with other tele-evangelists. The pimps today continuously strategize to try to maintain the loyalty factor, which leads to the art of pimping. The new word, Pimpogogy is the art and science of pimping. In this study, the pimping preacher can be seen constantly working to get people to have buy-in to maintaining his ministry.

━ Why do people attend church? ━

Since there are so many emotional, physical, social, economic and spiritual problems in our society, we try to deal with them through the psychiatrist, physician, counselor, or therapist. Unfortunately, such opportunities are not always readily affordable or available and the church is the alternative to address some of these problems. It is a place to deal with the rigors and perplexities of life. Recognizing that people need spiritual guidance and a leader to help them sets the stage for church and some who might look at this as an opportunity for self-aggrandizement. Even though there are those who sincerely do ministry, they sometimes find themselves being pulled them away from what is right. That is, a minister's ability to address the problems of the masses can be met with some corruption if that minister yields to the status quo in ministry. If a minister says something that appears to be sincere intentions, they can get the masses to do things to show they are in support of what he/she says, that is, they can sell the word for whatever price they see fit.

The depth of scriptures and tradition presents the environment for the masses who seek God and spiritual growth. Those who have researched and studied the word can still fall prey to the innuendos and "taken out of context" scripture traps. The churches have given preachers recognition beyond what the Bible teaches. That is, pastors who preach and teach with a sincere heart are still placed in a light that makes them appear more than human and the sad notion to all of this is that they are given attention to the point of minimizing the significance of what ministry should do for people. The people or the congregation encourages narcissistic preachers on several levels. They will support them when they do wrong. They will say "amen" to them even when they don't know what they are talking about. They will allow them to bamboozle money out of them without question. They will allow them to brainwash and trick them with scriptures even when the scriptures are not applicable to the situation.

People are less likely to stir up controversy against a popular preacher who leads good activities for the community. The congregation instills trust in everything that the visionary pastor purports and at the moment when something goes wrong, there are times when a percentage of the congregation will leave—with the feeling of betrayal. This shows that people should not have put their trust in the person from the beginning. Now the portion of the congregation that supports the wrongdoing pastor tends to be the ones who refuse to believe that any wrong has been done or will lean on the forgiveness factor. They are in denial and find themselves forgiving for reasons like: They simply like the person. They refuse to take a stance against a person they like so they'll pull out the good that the person has done and discount the indiscretion. They will say that the preacher who has done wrong deserves forgiveness just like all of us who have sinned and have been helped by the pastor.

Pastors who fit the description of pimp might welcome recognition and glory through the acceptance of gifts, notoriety, and a lifestyle that is far from moderation. If one were to recognize what Christendom entails, it would seem oxymoronic to consider a shepherd living a lifestyle that does not address preaching to the poor but rather taking from the poor. It is amazing how ministers use powerful and rich people of God in the Bible to make claims that prosperity is the means to being blessed. In fact, the prosperity gospel is now trending in our society but the term prosperity is misunderstood and solely linked to money. This type of preaching has swept the nation because it is popular to want to live a lifestyle that is far from impoverishment. When you see the popularity of how so many people play the lottery, participate in Publishers Clearing House and other prize-winning opportunities—it seems the human nature is to want to win something or get rich. So with this understanding, it is okay to realize that people want a quick solution to prosperity. We want quick answers to healing. We want instantaneous results for emotional and physical problems. So we really shouldn't be surprised when individuals capitalize on the weak nature of the human condition. Yes, the human condition has weaknesses and it is the opportunity for some to capitalize on it.

Why are only a few prospering or benefiting from the gospel while so many continue to suffer? The success of one person should bring about controversy as most of the supporting members are struggling under a fixed-income system. Additionally, there are pastors who welcome being appreciated annually by their members in the form of appreciation services in which the members plow money and gifts into the minister or pastor. It sets a tone that it is a requirement, and there is no scriptural basis for annual gift-giving. It distracts from the cheerful giving dynamic to a degree that people should not be prompted to give on a particular date simply because another decided to do so. This does not exemplify or support the one who does the work of the Lord. Gift giving when systematically done or of necessity, discredits the sincerity and purpose of giving and when one is able to give. If you are called by God to do the work, then your reward is in heaven. No one should have to reward you outside of a salary for the work that God has called you to do. Some will argue that God will prompt others to give to you, which is perfect but when you systematically feel the obligation to give a gift to satiate and win bonus points, you are giving with the wrong heart. You are trying to obtain the favor of man and not God.

A pastor who does the work of God should not have to live a lavish lifestyle. However, the view that there is nothing wrong with having nice things really leads to the idea that these things are borrowed as none of these items will be taken with you even if you desire to be adorned by them in a coffin when your number arises. The problem exists when one ostentatiously flashes these items before a congregation of people who are trying to find God. It exists when one has the mindset of material things and behaves to impress others with their material possessions. This is unquestionably a pimping dynamic. No one should have to look at that. Put on an abbey and sit down somewhere! It is a distraction when listening to what the preacher says while he is sporting a Rolex watch. It is a distraction when one is wearing a suit with a price tag that could easily pay someone's mortgage. It is a distraction when the clothing being worn is far from moderate apparel and at times reveals a sexual suggestion. Yes, wearing tight pants so that your genitals are showing or muscle shirts so that the lust factor is in effect. The simple notion of being flamboyant is reflective of a conceited individual who welcomes attention to him or herself. When in a pulpit and delivering the word of God, people should not have to contend with a pimp, player or any type of worldly type distraction. People should be able to leave the church with a sense of fulfillment from the Holy Word. Lastly, a pastor should not benefit from the masses that tend to struggle to pay bills and meet their needs while building up ministries with their giving. It seems that the vision is to build incredible structures that provide a comfortable platform for the members rather than reaching out to the people who have spiritual and physical needs.

Prologue

The setting begins around a medium-sized ministry with approximately three thousand members. The church has fifteen employees with half of the employees working on a part-time basis. The ministry is headed by Pastor Danig, who is the new pastor that recently graduated from Weldon-Craft Theological Seminary and is excited about the new position. The administrative assistant is a young female who was recently hired when the former assistant left the ministry over some issues with the former pastor. She works as an administrative assistant to the pastor. She is a single mom and is thankful to have a job where she can get experience with her administrative skills. She feels protected because she's working in an environment that cares for people. She sees how the ministry helps the poor and the sick and feels comfortable being in such a caring environment.

Scene outside of church:

Once upon a time, on a cold, early, and breezy Sunday morning in Brooklyn, New York, and cars are double-parked on the streets of Flatbush Avenue adjacent to an old-style theatre that was converted into a church. The two-lane street design with low curves with metal bordering around the cement made it easier for people to conveniently park their cars on a portion of the sidewalk in anticipation to make room for someone who would inevitably double-park next to them. People ignored the "No Double Parking" signs in desperation to find parking and to quickly get out of the cold. As Julya attempted to find parking, she drove cautiously in her wide, loosely steering Electra 225. The streets seemed narrower with all of the double parking and it seemed that no one cared about double parking next to someone and blocking them in. She began parallel parking at a visible space before the end of the block. After turning the key to the off position and grabbing her fake Dooney and Bourke, the insignia caught a metal snag from the worn vinyl seats. As she struggled to clear the purse, she squeezed out of the car, looking both ways for traffic and began walking briskly toward the church administrative offices.

Scene in church office:

Pastor Danig walks into his office and as Julya is organizing papers on her desk, she looks up and greets him with a smile and softly tells him, "Your wife left a message for you to call her as soon as you can."

Pastor Danig: "Okay, and good morning, Julya! How are you?"

Julya continues shuffling through papers and responds quietly with, "I'm fine!"

His response came with an encouraging sounding innuendo, "Well, I'm blessed and highly favored, how about you?"

Julya smiles and says, "Me too, Pastor!"

Pastor Danig: "Well, I'll see you at the meeting in an hour!"

He goes in his study and makes the call and his wife, Maylee gets on the phone complaining about him tending to everyone's needs in the ministry and never really having time for family things. She complains, "Aren't you the pastor and can't you just take off today? You just got back from a three-day conference in Chicago!"

He said, "I have a responsibility to the ministry and I need to be here to deal with the issues of the church."

She snarled, "Well, what are the assistant pastors doing? You can't do all of the work!"

He said, "They have their duties and I must tell you that the assistant pastors are not equipped to do some of the things that I have to do as the head pastor."

She said with an urgent voice, "I don't believe that! If you are in charge, why don't you allocate some of those duties to your capable ministers?"

With a raised eyebrow and firmness in his voice, he responded, "Okay, so now you're telling me how to do ministry! You don't think I know this and that if I was able, I would do just that! I don't think you really understand but I would love to be home spending time with family but my role as pastor and my obedience to God doesn't always allow me to be with my family as I desire!"

She then said, "Really! Is that what you really think?"

He raised his voice slightly and said, "So now you're hearing from God about what God has to do in my life. You came into this marriage knowing what a pastor's wife's lifestyle would be like! This is all of the stuff we covered in premarital counseling and you acted as though you were onboard and now all of a sudden you're changing?"

She began crying hysterically and said, "You really don't understand. I've been supportive of you all of these years and you don't really appreciate it! I've patiently stayed home caring for the children while you were out on conference business trips doing church business. You never invited me to any of these conferences and I thought the church was about family. Do the other ministers bring their wives or do you pastors go on these business trips to get away from your wives and spend time doing other things like womanizing? I don't understand what this ministry thing is all about but I thought the Bible said that a husband should love his wife like Christ loved the church!"

As Pastor Danig's anger started to increase, he responded with, "Womanizing! Where did this come from? I have not womanized on any of these business trips!"

Maylee: "So you've womanized elsewhere?"

Pastor Danig pauses for a moment and responds, "I'm not womanizing anywhere or in any environment! I'm out there doing God's work and the only thing you can come up with is womanizing! I'm appalled at such a remark and if I'm doing God's work, don't you think that this is indicative of me loving you like Christ loved the church?" He then refrained from an angry voice and said, "I will talk to you more about this after the meeting. I have to go."

Maylee: "Why are you going so abruptly? The meeting doesn't start for another thirty minutes!

"But honey," he said calmly, "I have to prepare for the meeting! I can't just walk in there! I have to go—I will call you later...."

With a confused and frustrated look on his face, he quickly hangs up the phone and then tries to correct it so that he would not alert anyone of the tension in his marriage. Pastor Danig continued with the confused look and then walked out of his office toward his administrative assistant and said, "Can you type this agenda up for me as soon as possible?"

She responds with an innocent and sweet-sounding voice, "Sure, Pastor, I'll have it ready for you right away. Is there anything else you'd like me to do?"

The pastor smiles and says, "No, and thank you for helping me out on this one! I got caught up on a phone call that took me away from doing it myself. I usually like putting the agenda together myself because it is what I do as I'm scheduling the meeting. I'll see you in 15 minutes."

Pastor Danig then walks over to the snack machine and grabs a coffee and some chips. He sits down for a few minutes and while putting cream in the coffee, Julya walks over with the document in a folder and says, "It's complete, Pastor!"

Pastor Danig then pauses for a minute and looks at Julya with an inquisitive eye. He briefly thinks to himself, "I wonder what it would be if my wife was this pleasant? She is so polite and she doesn't argue with me. She pleasantly does what I ask without all of the drama. But I'm her supervisor, so perhaps she is just exhibiting some professionalism at the workplace." He then ponders of how he will learn more of his administrative assistant. He wants her to attend the next out-of-town meeting with him. "I will put her in her own room and give her carte-blanch treatment. It will be an experience for her because she has never done any business travel and this might be an opportunity for me to find out more about her during this trip." Pastor Danig thinks to himself, "I am the CEO of this corporation and I have the power to set things up like this. It is great being in charge. Yes, I am in charge doing the work of God and there are fringe benefits."

He leans over and takes the folder from his administrative assistant and thanks her with a smile and a wink. She walks away swinging her buttocks in a way that she knew he'd be looking. His thoughts began running amuck as he imagined what it would be like if he had a woman like this. He did not know her well enough to summarize what she'd be like but in his frustration, he imagined her to be something more than his wife. Maylee was someone who bickered and complained because her husband was not around in the manner that she imagined. Maylee was not the supportive wife that she initially purported to be. His thoughts wandered away from the stress that he felt his wife gave him with strategizing how he would get closer to the administrative assistant.

Scene – Pastor's home:

Maylee is home helping the children with homework and the oldest child falls out of the treehouse and is screaming to the top of his lungs. Maylee runs outside while the food is cooking on the stove and tells her daughter, "Keep an eye on the food!" She dashes out through the screen door and runs to help her son. He was acting as though he was dying but just panicking after the wind was knocked out of him from the fall. In her hysteria, she starts screaming but when she realized he was okay, she yelled, "I want you to stay out of that treehouse! You're going to get killed because you don't know how to use the ladder! I told you a dozen times not to climb into the treehouse on the branches." Her daughter could be seen peering through the window with a smirk on her face as if she wanted to laugh but held back because of her mother's serious disposition.

Scene switches to the boardroom:

Pastor Danig takes his seat at the head of a wooden oak table in a leather rotating business class seat. The deacons open up the meeting with a prayer and then begin the meeting with Parliamentary procedure. The deacon begins by noting a quorum to commence the meeting as twelve members are present. As the deacons bring up the building fund strategy plan, the pastor in his distracted moment isn't paying attention to what the deacon said and asks him to repeat his plan. As the meeting is going on, Pastor Danig is staring at his smartphone and reading messages from his wife. He looks up and gazes at his administrative assistant and is distracted. He acknowledges something the deacon said but his answer was not consistent with what the deacon said. His distraction put him in the mode where his mind wasn't focused on the meeting but rather the stress in his marriage and a justified opportunity to pursue his administrative assistant. The deacon said, "We need to get the members to support us in giving so that we can raise money for the initial down payment for the new building. The Lord has given the pastor the vision that the new facility will be in the Greenhill community." The deacon asked Pastor Danig, "So what are your thoughts about a location other than Greenhill that is larger and has better terms? We don't have to raise any money to get into this building and they are interested in leasing to us because we have good credit."

Pastor Danig said, "Huh? Well, I'm a bit confused! The Lord put on my heart the Greenhill location and although this new facility has the easier terms and is larger, I don't want to move away from the vision that God has given me!"

The deacon replied, "Well, as part of the vision of the church in reaching out to more people and expanding our school, the vision you have on Greenhill will not meet the needs of what we are trying to do at this facility."

Well, Pastor Danig replied, "I don't think you understand. The Greenhill location gives us an opportunity to expand out and build the school to our specifications. We have more flexibility with the school and the worship center."

"Well, Pastor," uttered the deacon, "why should we spend so much building and putting so much stress on the members to raise all of this money when a building is already built and the terms are better? Why must we build from scratch when it has already been done for us? The city is charging us fees upon fees and research on the land costs more than the down payment and then the land has to be prepared before building on it. There is the possibility that we won't be able to build on the land after we spend an enormous amount of money on research! What will we do if we spend so much money on the research and then find out that in a worst-case scenario that it is some sacred archeological site that won't allow any type of construction or disturbance of the land? We won't be able to build on the land! We would have exhausted all of this money which could be used to get the building that we're leasing in order."

Pastor Danig said, "So now you're telling me that the vision God has given me for this ministry is changing because you feel you have a better, cost-effective, environmentally friendly deal? I'm going to stick to the plan for the move forward with the Greenhill location."

The deacon responded, "You need to reconsider and not be narrow-minded on this issue.

"Well, I don't think I would be the pastor if this was democratic decision and further, your thinking should not be broad as narrow is the way in this case. We have to realize that the devil will deceive you into thinking that something looks good when in fact the underlying situation could be disastrous. We have to be reminded that I am your pastor and you have to trust how God speaks to me concerning this ministry. I'm asking for your support and your ideas will be respected but don't feel that I've done something wrong because you don't agree with me." Pastor Danig continues with trying to get the board members to yield to his whim. Pastor Danig: "We need to pray that we not usurp the authority of the pastor and that we don't get stuck on what we feel is right." He then said with a firm and confident voice, "Now I would like to make a motion to move forward with the Greenhill location."

The presiding leader said, "The motion has been set to move forward with the Greenhill location, All in favor say 'I.'"

Six of the members said, "I," while the remaining sat with either confused, angry or fearful looks on their faces.

"Now I'm going to ask that we visit the other items on the agenda at the next meeting."

The deacon had a perturbed look on his face and reluctantly agreed. Pastor Danig looked over at Julya as she worked on the minutes to the meeting. She maintained a smile while typing what he was saying.

The pastor looked over at her and asked, "Can you email the minutes to the attendees and I would like to meet with you in my office when you're done."

Scene in Pastor Danig's office:

Pastor Danig asked Julya to have a seat and then told her, "I would like to thank you for your excellent and prompt work here. Since we've hired you, you have made my work in this ministry so much easier and I don't know what I would do if I didn't have you as my assistant. You are detail-oriented, punctual, and pleasant to work with. Can you check your calendar and see if you're available October 23rd through the 27th for a three-day conference in Seattle? I need my righthand person to help me with things on this conference. This is an all-expense-paid trip for you as you will have your own room and you will get per diem."

She responded by saying, "I'm going to need to check and see if my sister will be able to babysit my children for three days."

Pastor Danig responded, "Well, let me know and if you're having problems with getting someone to watch the children. I know someone who's great with children and someone I trust who will be able to watch the children for those three days. If you don't like that arrangement you can bring them along."

She smiled and in her naivety she could not believe that the pastor would take these measures to see that she would make it to this conference. In her mind she thought that this is so cool that ministries would be so nice to go these extra measures to make a business trip possible and pay for everything. She was excited because she always dreamed about going on a business trip on her job.

Julya: "Mom, I was wondering if you would be able to help with the children because my job is sending me on a business trip in October for three days."

Mom replies, "Three days? What kind of business trip is this that will have you away for three days? It sounds really important."

"Well, Mom, I'm the administrative assistant to the pastor and they have me doing some really important stuff with setting up the meetings—the agenda, PowerPoint and stuff. The pastor needs me since I'm the backbone to the keeping things in order and flowing."

Mom replies, "So your pastor asked you to do this?"

Julya excitingly responds, "Oh, yes, Mom, and he told me in today's meeting that he was pleased with my organizational skills."

Mom sighs, "So he told you that?" She pauses and shuffles through some papers. "Well, I need to check with the other nurses to see if I can swap hours because I planned to work extra so I can have some extra money for the holiday season."

"So you will do it, Mom?"

"I'll let you know tomorrow. I need to look at the schedule and see if a nurse will swap with me! Anyway, I want you to promise me something. I know you're a grown woman and you can take care of yourself but these business trips at hotels worry me a little. I've heard of pastors messing around with their secretaries and people in their company and I don't want you getting mixed up in no mess."

She responds, "Mom, this pastor is not like that and he's married. He loves the Lord and is very committed to the ministry. I must say that he's not like some of those pastors you might have heard of."

Mom responds, "Okay, sweetie, I just thought I'd tell you to just be careful."

Julya sighs, "Okay, Mom, I'll be careful, and remember I would not put myself in a situation where I'm the other woman for some temporary benefits. I had my problems already being involved with a man who lied to me about being single and then when I got pregnant, he decided to confess. He said he was not leaving his wife and treated me like I was a tramp. This pastor is married and I think you know me, Mom—I wouldn't put myself in a situation like that."

Mom: "Okay, baby, I've heard you well but again, be careful because things happen so quickly—you find yourself not wanting to do something and then you sometimes end up doing it because you're vulnerable. You've placed yourself in situations that you think you're strong enough to deal with and then when it's happening—your emotions and your current situation sometimes causes you to think and behave otherwise. You have to be careful, honey, because these men know what they're doing. They study the word of God and they have a degree of wisdom that they will use to manipulate those whom they wish to take advantage of. I say all of this because I know a personal friend who had an issue with a man of the cloth and she ended up being the other woman who consented to a relationship with a pastor who she knew was married. He lied to her in such a way that made it seem that he would divorce his wife and marry this woman. This pastor was a player and he was also on the down-low. He did things secretly and thought no one would ever find out because the people in his company supported his behavior. It was like a code of silence amongst the clergy members. In fact, they all participated in this riotous lifestyle where money was being spent on traveling and conferences and using the church credit card to mask their behavior. There were no checks and balances because the people who were auditing the books were the people who worked in the church and they knew all of the corruption but no one ever said a word. They felt that these men needed to have some fun since they're doing all these incredible things in the ministry—helping people and preaching the word. Why should we stand against a person who's doing all of this wonderful things by exposing their personal lifestyle?"

Julya responds with a perturbed look on her face, "Mom, I think you're taking an isolated situation and you're trying to apply it to the ministry that I work for. They're not involved in this type of corruption and I would not work in a ministry that is corrupt like that. I have my degree and I can work almost anywhere I'm needed."

Mom replies, "Well, sweetie, how long have you been working there?"

Julya, "I've been there for three months."

"Okay, well, sweetie, you haven't been there long enough to see what's really going on. In fact, I'm not saying that your church ministry is corrupt but I just want you to keep your awareness heightened. I don't want you to fall in the same trap that so many vulnerable woman fall into. You're a single mom trying to do the right thing and some of these pastors will use that to their advantage. They see a good woman trying to be both parents in the household and dedicated to raising her children. A pastor or someone who is in a powerful position might take advantage of this especially if he sees the opportunity to make a move. He might make an attempt and if the door is open slightly, he might simply push his way through. You have to make a decision whether you will give him such an opportunity or will you stand your ground."

"Mom, you're talking to me like this pastor is interested in me like that?"

"No, I'm not saying that the pastor is interested in you and perhaps he's not interested in you at all but don't be naïve over compliments about your work and so on. I have to go, sweetie, but just keep in mind what I said and don't worry—it's just something I thought I'd share with you because the world is not always what it seems."

Scene at Pastor Danig's home:

The pastor arrives home and greets his wife at the entrance. She says, "Honey, I think we should eat out today and spend a little quality time together. Jan said she'll watch the kids."

Pastor Danig: "Honey, I'm really tired and don't feel like going anywhere tonight—can we just stay home and talk tonight?"

Maylee: "Yes, but the things we need to talk about, I don't want to talk about around the children. These are sensitive matters and I just want to go someplace and be in a different environment while I let it out of my system."

Pastor Danig hesitantly responds, "Honey, are you trying to go there with our earlier conversation because I really don't want to argue or labor the issue. We've been through this over and over again and the lifestyle of a pastor or pastor's wife was not intended to be easy."

Maylee says, "Honey, I'm going to the car and I'll wait for you."

Pastor Danig concedes and goes into the bathroom, washes his hands and says, "Okay, give me a minute while I change quickly."

Maylee says, "Okay, you do that and I'll wait patiently—you know patience is a virtue."

The pastor ponders about patience and virtue and how the two words mean something different. In his analysis, he then says, "And what are you saying?"

She ignores his comment and walks out to the car and the neighbor who's sitting on the porch greets her with an enthusiastic hello. She's an older woman with a very dainty and sophisticated demeanor. The sound of classical piano music is usually heard coming from her house on a daily basis. She comes out of her door and says to Maylee, "How are you today?"

Maylee smiles and says, "Fine."

Neighbor: "You look lovely! Are you and your husband going out?"

Maylee quickly responds, "Yes, we're finally getting a chance to get something to eat that's prepared by someone else. I just need a little break from it all."

The neighbor says, "Well, darling, you deserve a break and it's good that you and your husband are going out. You guys seem like the ideal couple and one day, I'm going to come down to that church."

Maylee responds, "Well, that's very sweet of you and we would love to have you."

The neighbor pauses for a second and then says, "Can I ask you a question?"

Maylee says, "Sure."

The neighbor proceeded to ask several questions. Neighbor: "What's it like being married to a preacher? Do you find your life a bit boring and always by the book or do you and your husband do things that are fun?"

Maylee, in her attempt to respond, was interrupted by the neighbor for some additional questions.

Neighbor: "Don't Christians live boring lives? I can't see myself being married to someone who's always talking about the Bible and trying to live right by some else's standards. Aren't these men of God just fooling themselves into trying to live this consecrated lifestyle that they know is impossible?"

Maylee finally gets her response in. Maylee: "Well, all things are possible with God and I think we have to try to live right instead of making excuses about how impossible things are."

The neighbor jumped in with an insidious judgmental response. Neighbor: "Well, that's what I'm talking about, all things are possible can mean just that. All things corrupt can be possible and so a man of God might lead a life of corruption and believe that all things are possible. They can live any lifestyle and God will forgive them and let them into heaven." She continues. Neighbor: "I think that's corrupt and how pastors will tend to twist scriptures to their benefit."

Maylee realizes the time is limited for the response she would like to give and then responds. Maylee: "Well, I can invite you to the Wednesday Bible class and we can get clarification on some of these scriptures because I know that man's flesh is weak and we need God to help us with our issues. I know none of us are perfect and that God rewards those who diligently seek him."

Her husband walks out the door and while he approaches them, the neighbor asks her final question.

Neighbor: "Why would God create such corrupt, imperfect humans that make all of these mistakes if He is so pure, perfect, and without corruption?"

"C'mon, honey, we're going to be late for our dinner appointment."

"Hey, I'll talk to you later...."

The Escalade backs slowly out of the driveway and the elderly lady waves as they pull off.

Scene at the deacon's home:

The deacon is sitting on the brown, plush leather couch in his living room. His wife is in the kitchen working on some the juicing machine. The deacon starts complaining about the church meeting and how the pastor dismissed his idea about the direction of the church. He said that the church can avoid spending unnecessary money by moving to the other location. The deacon's wife simply listened to his complaint and then responded, "This is what these pastors do in ministry. They simply have the last word on everything, so don't take it personal, honey."

The deacon replies, "No, I realize that but it is the people who are supporting these ministries headed by these pastors and I think that it is unfair to the people to have someone be so narrow-minded about ministry stuff that affects those who are supporting the ministry. We're planning on spending an enormous amount of money on starting from scratch and we might end up not being able to build on the property anyway. Will that mean that God was not speaking to this pastor and that he simply wanted this church to be on this site simply because it was a nice location and it looked good in his eyes? How do we really know that God is speaking through this pastor?"

His wife responds, "Well, do you believe that your pastor is a man of God? Do you know that he is communing with the Lord? If you believe otherwise then perhaps you should not follow him and maybe you should take your concerns up with the board or even schedule a meeting with the pastor. Better yet, voice your concerns to him directly!"

He responds, "Honey, maybe you're right, because I really don't feel comfortable about the direction of this ministry. I know that I'm not the pastor but I am an important decision-maker in the church and feel that the money has already been misspent on foolishness. I have to say something and I must take a stand against this type of behavior. Pastor Danig thinks he has all of the answers and if he did he wouldn't need a committee or a board with members—who have a voice. We are useless if our voices don't make a sense in the meeting. He needs just be the pastor and not have any advisors or board members for that matter. This is all some sort of joke or scheme to make it look like the board members are in agreement on something so the members won't feel a dictatorial feel on major decisions in the church."

She responds, "Well, honey, don't stress out over it! If God is in control, then all of your concerns will not fall on deaf ears. The outcome will show God's glory in all of this. Sometimes we don't understand and since God is supposed to be at the forefront in these ministries and if you believe that, then your concerns will have an impact. If the church is what the Bible says it is and the gates of hell shall not prevail against it, then all of the silly, corrupt stuff you see might be permitted by God but he will get the glory when the time is right. I think God allows us to make silly mistakes and then we go back to him asking for forgiveness and only he has the power to do that even though we still have to suffer the consequences for our sins. There is a problem when we really don't listen to the voice of God. It is a shame how we separate ourselves from God through our on fleshly desires. If the pastor has a desire to do something that is outside of the will of God...."

The deacon interrupts, "That's what I'm talking about! Why should the people have to pay for the mistakes of one person who has a vision that might be outside of the will of God?"

His wife jumps in, "Well, you really don't know if it is outside of the will of God! I don't think people are paying for the mistake of another. If they follow a leader, then they have willingly decided to put their trust in a man they believe to be a man of God. I think if we think too hard about this we'll drive ourselves crazy wondering about the 'what ifs' all the time."

The deacon continues, "Well, the 'what ifs' are important! We shouldn't simply sit back and relax and just let stupid stuff happen! We shouldn't let people manipulate or sway us in a direction without asking questions."

She sighs, "I think you're right, honey, now let's go to bed! I'm tired of all of this church drama and I think we need to relieve some stress!"

The deacon raises his eyebrow as if she was talking about a nightcap.

Deacon's wife: "Actually, we need a break and your job is taking your focus away from your family and it is family time!"

He agrees and walks into the other room where the children are playing. He sits down next to his son and asks him, "What do you want to be when you grow up?"

He says, "I want to be a preacher."

He looks over at his wife and says, "Honey, let's pray and kids, let's get ready for bed, it's late and we have school tomorrow."

Scene—Morning scene at the church:

It's moments before 7 A.M. on Monday morning and the dew can be seen clearing in the distance around the church grounds. Julya sees Pastor Danig as she approaches the building. He waves from a distance and enters the building. As she enters the building, the stagnant putrid septic tank odor filled the hallway. It didn't seem to bother anyone as this odor was the first thing one would smell when entering the building and nothing had been done to rectify the problem for years.

Pastor Danig: "Good morning! How was your weekend?"

Julya responds, "It was good and anyway, Pastor, I'll know by tomorrow if I'll be able to get someone to watch my children."

Pastor Danig: "Great, I really would like you to be on this conference! There's so much to learn and I think it will minister to you even though you'll be there in a work capacity."

She thought to herself that this pastor is not one of those phony preachers trying to make a move on her. "I think my mother was a bit intense when she shared her friend's experience with me." After a moment of daydreaming, she responded, "Thanks, Pastor, I'm sure I'll be able to get my mother to watch the children—she said that she needed to confirm her work hours with the other nurses on her job."

Pastor Danig: "Okay, just let me know and I'll talk to you later!"

He rushed off to his office and she went to the snack machine and purchased a coffee. While waiting for the machine to heat up the coffee she could see on the table in the office next door a FedEx package that had her name on it. It had inscribed, "ATTENTION: Julya Goodman." She was wondering what this package was all about but it was in the office next door and the door was locked. She peered through the glass pane and saw conference materials and in her mind she said, "Hmmm, they've already scheduled me for this conference even though I haven't confirmed babysitting arrangements with my mom. I guess the pastor was serious about having someone watch my children if my mom didn't work out."

Scene: Dinner at an elegant restaurant at the Marina:

The restaurant waitress says, "Seating for two?"

"Yes, for once in our lives!" says Maylee. "I can't remember the last outing we were on when it was just the two of us and no church folk. Whew, and I hope I don't see anyone here today."

After being seated, Maylee excuses herself from the table and said to her husband, "Honey, can you order a raspberry iced tea for me? I'll be right back."

"Sure," he replies, and then he reaches for his smartphone. He looks at the phone and notices 13 missed calls. One of the calls is from Julya, which read, "Can I get the password to the computer? My password expired and no one is available to help me with this." He then scrolls through the rest of the missed calls and switches over to Facebook. He leaves a message that he's spending an evening with his wife and while he's typing it, Maylee returns and says, "Honey, can you please put the phone away so we can spend time together?"

He says, "I need to check my messages—what type of pastor doesn't check his messages? There could be a major emergency and I wouldn't know anything about it. It only takes a second just to check some messages, hun—please relax."

She says, "I cannot relax because you're on Facebook telling the world what we're doing."

He responds, "Do you think that's right for you to be watching me so closely—I'm posting something so that people will not disturb me."

Maylee, "Okay, if you don't want anyone to disturb you, you don't have to tell the world, just put the phone away!"

He then says, "I don't think you should monitor what I'm doing on my phone. Out of respect, you should let me handle my business and stop nagging and monitoring everything that I do."

She stares at him and pauses for a moment, "Nagging? So now I'm nagging and just so you know, I'm not monitoring what you're doing! You're doing it right in my face, Facebook! Look, I didn't arrange this dinner date so that we would argue. I just want us to sit down in a nice setting and talk about some things that are concerning me in our marriage and the ministry."

Pastor Danig: "We could've talked about all of this at home in a more private setting."

Maylee: "Well, this is private enough and what we're talking about is going to be general stuff and I think it might make the conversation more enjoyable and with less distractions like the kids, the TV or the computer."

Pastor Danig: "Okay, I'll try to avoid distractions while we enjoy this evening together."

Maylee: "Honey, I think you're being sarcastic and you don't really care what I'm trying to do."

Pastor Danig then says, "What you're trying to do?"

Maylee: "Yes, what I'm trying to do—I'm trying to protect our marriage!"

Pastor Danig: "Oh, so what are you saying? Our marriage is in trouble? Why is our marriage in trouble, honey?"

She contorts, "Well, our dinner date might bring that to light."

He stares at her with a perplexed look as if she knew something on the lines of his interaction with Julya. Perhaps her intuition was kicking in before an event or just the feeling of him being more devoted to his work instead of working on their marriage.

The waitress approaches and asks, "Can I get you something to drink?"

Pastor Danig responded, "Yes, and I'm ready to order." He then looks over at his wife and asks, "Are you ready to order, honey?"

Maylee: "Yes, I already know what I want and it's my favorite platter!"

After ordering and the waitress leaves, he tells her, "I don't understand what you're talking about when you said our marriage is in trouble."

She says, "I did not say our marriage is in trouble—I said I want to protect our marriage. Maybe you feel our marriage is in trouble since you're saying it!"

"Well, you might not have said our marriage is in trouble but by saying that it needs protecting sounds like it is in trouble. I have value in what we've committed to in this marriage and I feel that you are disinterested in our happiness. You seem to be more involved with your work and before you know it, the people that you interact on your job will have more importance than your own family. I feel like you're straying away from your family."

Pastor Danig: "Okay, you have arranged this wonderful dinner to get away and protect our marriage so I would like to hear you out, honey. Okay, so I'm going to be quiet and let you talk first."

She then pauses and says, "I know when we took our marriage vow that I would be there for you and I really think that you're neglecting your family as far as time goes. We never get to see you! When you started out in ministry, you did your visitations and conferences and so on but it was never to this magnitude. Lately, you have been away from your family more than ever. It seems that the ministry is your new wife and family. I think when a ministry grows, you have to allocate some of those responsibilities to the other pastors—you can't do it all. It seems like you're going to more and more conferences and we are seeing less and less of you! When will you say no to all of these demands that this ministry is putting on you?" She pauses and awaits his response and he just stares at her as if she spoke in another tongue.

Before he could respond, a church member runs up to the table and says, "How are you doing, Pastor and Sister Maylee? I can't wait to go to the conference! So when are you guys flying out?"

"Well, Sister Bethel, actually Maylee and the kids aren't going to make this one but I'll be flying out a day earlier to make preparations."

"Okay, well, that's good, I guess, but I won't bother you guys! I just couldn't help but say hello when I saw you guys from over there!"

As she walks away, Maylee says something under her breath, "I thought we got away from these interruptions! What's next? Is she going to ask you to join them for dinner? I don't understand. Are you going to respond to my concerns?"

As Pastor Danig was looking down with his glasses slightly off his nose, he said in a low voice, "Oh, honey, can you repeat that last thing that you said, the interruption from the church member made me lose track of what you said. I want to make sure I address your concerns."

Maylee then said, "I'm tired of you not listening to me and your phone is vibrating. Why don't you just turn it off?"

Pastor Danig: "I'm not answering, hun, and I'm trying to hear you out."

"Well, can you please turn it off? You don't need to know that someone is calling you right now! At least for the next couple of hours, you should just turn it off!"

He reaches for the phone and, before he actually turns it off, begins reading the missed call list. He says, "Hold on, honey, I need to return this call."

She said, "I can't believe you're actually going to return a call!" She asks with a slight raised voice, "Who is it?"

He says, "Honey, it is church business and I must get the call now! Please give me a break! I'm trying to take care of a situation before it gets out of control!"

Maylee: "Oh, okay, so now there's an emergency? What type of emergency is it? Tell them to call 911—my husband is unavailable!"

"I'll be back," he says, and runs from the table to get the call from his administrative assistant." He stands in the parking lot and says, "How are you? What's going on?"

Julya: "Well, Pastor, I just found out that my mother can watch the children and I was trying to get into the computer so I can get started on the media materials for the conference. My password expired—can you help me?"

Pastor Danig said, "Sure, I'll call our IT guy and have him reset the password for you. Call me or text me in about 15 minutes and let me know if he was able to help you with this. Okay, I must go so that I can call him."

Julya says, "Okay, thank you, Pastor Danig."

He speed dials his IT guy while he's walking back to his table and Maylee is staring at him with a catatonic look on her face. He sits down with the phone pressed to his ear and begins leaving a message.

"Hey, Din, give me a call as soon as possible. I need you to reset the password for my administrative assistant to expedite work on some media files. Please text me and let me know that you were able to do this."

He presses the pound sign and the voice on the other side could be heard, message sent, thank you for calling, goodbye. He then presses the end button on the phone and holds it.

"Okay, hun, I won't answer the phone anymore—I just shut it off. No calls will disturb us for the rest of the evening."

Maylee responds, "So you just told your IT guy to text you as soon as he's able for a password reset. So you're going to be thinking about whether he was able to reset the password for work that must be done for this conference. You're going to be thinking about all of this stuff and not paying much attention to what I'm saying. You might as well turn your phone on and wait for the response that you're looking for because right now, everything seems to be centered on ministry and I'm secondary or the family is secondary."

Pastor Danig: "Okay, now honey," he says, "I think you're overreacting just a bit! I am here for this family and my responsibility is to our family. This is work-related stuff and I have to do these things so that the ministry functions. Our livelihood is contingent upon things running smoothly in this ministry. So look at it as a job in addition to the ministry stuff. If I stop what I'm doing and things go wrong in the ministry, then who's going to pay the bills around here?"

"Hold on a second," she says, and then he interrupts, "Why are you raising your voice? I thought this was a discussion and we are in a public place. I'm a pastor and some of our members could be in the audience."

She responds, "In the audience? Oh, so you want to put on a front about everything. You want to present yourself as the available and loving pastor and yet you can't even here me out. You want all of your members to be pleased while your family goes on neglected. I don't care about you paying some bills because you think you have to do everything to hold the ministry together. No man is an island and all of those people you have working in the ministry—they can step up to the plate and get it done." Again, he says, "You're trying to tell me how to do my job and I don't want to talk about this anymore.

Let's just eat and discuss it later. There are members here and I don't want them in our business. I don't get it anyway, why would we come to a dinner to discuss something like this? You know I'm a public figure and the walls have ears, you know! I don't want my business in the street and I want to remain private. Do us both a favor and let's drop it!"

She looks at him with a disappointed stare. He reaches down and picks up his phone and turns it back on. She then says, "It's so amazing how you make time for YOUR church people. You never cease to amaze me!"

Pastor Danig: "Honey, I said let's drop it for now. Yep, that's all you want to do is put stuff off when it comes to us. I'm not even going to enjoy this meal."

The waiter stops by the table with the food and she says firmly, "Can you box my order? I'm ready to go and bring the check, please."

Before the waitress can say something he jumps in and says, "Box both orders, please!"

She sits there and stares with a perturbed look on her face. He then ignores the stare and looks into his smartphone and begins returns a text message to Julya, who said that she did not hear from Din. He began typing a response that said, "You don't have to wait for the IT guy to get back to you since you're ready to set things in motion. I'm going to give you my login information and will trust that you will delete it from your phone. I will change my password after you've finished using it as a protective measure, but I'll give it to you now so that you can access the files you need for the conference." He types in the username and password.

Maylee is looking at him as he's texting and says, "Honey, may I ask what you're doing?"

He says, "Honey, since we're not talking about our problems now, I've decided to make use of this time to finish solving the problem we had with the church."

She said, "I realize that, but what are you doing?"

"Well, it's really no concern of yours but if you must know, I'm giving my password to the administrative assistant so they can access important files for use at the conference."

Maylee: "They?"

Pastor Danig continues past her inquiry of "they." "This has to be done because there is much preparation that needs to take place. Now can I—"

She interrupts, "You mean to tell me that you just gave your administrative assistant, or should I say 'they,' your password information?" I've never heard of anyone texting passwords! I thought this was sensitive information."

Pastor Danig: "Yes, you're right, it is sensitive information but it had to be done so that the work can get done. I trust my administrative assistant with the files that she already has access to with her password, which simply needs to be reset. The IT guy is unavailable to do this, so I've made the decision to give her access to the files."

She raises her eyebrows and surprisingly says, "Her? I thought your administrative assistant was a guy. What happened to the guy?"

He then says, "What difference does it make?"

"Well, it doesn't make a difference."

He then replies, "I don't get it."

Maylee: "Never mind and before I forget, I have two tickets to the comedy club. It's down the street and starts in about an hour, so can we just finish our meal?"

Danig: "Comedy club! Since when do we go to comedy clubs? You know what type of environments those are! The comedians are cursing and talking about sex and drugs. Come on, Maylee...."

Maylee interrupts, "Now hold it right there. Do you honestly think that I would get tickets to a raunchy comedy? Maybe you need some of that! You'll probably relax a little."

Danig: "What's that supposed to mean?"

Maylee: "It means you don't trust your wife! I did this dinner and comedy thing so that you and I can spend an evening together—something to break up the monotony."

Pastor Danig: "Well, I don't think we should be going to comedy clubs. It's an appearance of evil and I don't want to run into any more church folks while we're trying to spend quality time together."

Maylee: "Well, don't worry, the comedy is clean. In fact, it's Christian comedy and that's what I mean—you don't even trust me. You thought I would get tickets to some raunchy stuff and you're the pastor. Now the reason I should be in place like that is if we were doing some witnessing or something."

Pastor Danig: "So now we're going to a Christian comedy—so much for not seeing church folk."

Maylee: "You're probably looking forward to seeing some church folks."

Pastor Danig: "Okay, perhaps we don't need to go to this Christian comedy because your sarcasm is getting on my nerves!"

Maylee: "The jokes on me, hun, and so now we need to go where the jokes on others, which might lighten things up a bit around here!"

Pastor Danig: "Okay, so now we're going to a place that might have comedy that should help us with our problems."

Maylee: "Maybe—you know how these comedians talk about stuff that many of us are going through—so let's go and have a good time. You never know what might come of it."

Pastor Danig sighs and says, "Okay, I'm just going to go along with all of this and go with the flow." He thinks silently, "My wife is trying to do something nice, so I'm going to relax and go with the flow. There's no telling what might come of this."

Scene: At the comedy store:

Pastor Danig and his wife are seated at the front tables. They are only several feet from the stage. The environment is dimly lit in the audience while the more intense lighting it toward the tables near the stage. Pastor Danig and his wife are sitting drinking iced teas while the music begins to fade. The announcer comes on the stage and is warming up the crowd. He then introduces the comedian as the music is playing. The music stops and the comedian screams at the crowd and as he is talking Pastor Danig looks over at his wife and says, "I hope this comedian doesn't come over here with his jokes and tries to say something to us. I'm not in the mood for comedians using their comedy on me right now."

Maylee: "Relax, hun. Let's just have a good time."

The comedian runs on the stage and begins looking around the audience and compliments the audience by saying, "You all look very lovely today—well, at least most of you! You know some of you look stressed! We came here to have a good time, so let's have fun!" He looks at a man in the audience with strong prescription glasses for nearsightedness and says, "Sir, can you see me? What type of glasses are those? I can't even see your eyes, damn, oh, did I just curse? Well, you need to get on a prayer line! Somebody got some mud

22 | DAWUD AASIYA-BEY

up in here?" He then looks over at a heavyset man who looked nearly 400 pounds. He said, "Sir, can I pray for you?"

The man started looking around as if he didn't know that the comedian was calling him out. The heavyset man said, "Who me?"

The comedian then said, "No, all three of you!" The comedian began speaking in a preacher's voice and said, "I'm going to say it again, and I need you to obey the words of the prophet—all of you come up here now!"

The crowd begins laughing aloud and the heavyset man laughs along and takes it in stride. He gets up from his seat and approaches the stage and then stands before the comedian as if he was next in line on a prayer line.

The comedian continues talking with a deep-sounding prophetic voice and says, "I'm going to pray healing in your life over your weight problem. Are you ready to be healed from this disorder? I'm going to speak life into your life because your weight problem is going to get you killed." He then asks the heavyset man, "Do you believe that you have a weight problem?"

The heavyset man looks at him and wonders if the comedian is joking or serious and responds, "Yes."

The comedian then says, "Your problem is that you cannot wait to eat! Let me pray for you."

Some people in the audience were laughing while others had looks of pity for the heavyset man.

The comedian then said, "Okay, this is comedy but I must confess to all of you that I used to be 450 pounds and I lost 210 pounds so I know what this gentleman might be going through." He gave the man a card and told him to contact him after the show and then said, "Let's give him a hand for being a good sport over a problem that many suffer. Okay, so what's the deal with women who walk around pregnant and don't even know it?" He begins speaking loudly, "I don't get it, how do you walk around for nine months and you're pregnant and you don't know it until the moment it is time to have the baby? I mean, don't babies move around in you and kick and do summersaults and what have you?" He says with greater emphasis, "How do you NOT know that you're pregnant?"

The crowd laughs as he makes an insane face with his eyes stretched.

He continues, "Is the baby one of those stealth, Special Forces babies just secretly hiding out in the womb and just slips out in the ninth month? What's that all about?"

The camera zooms in on a pregnant lady, who's laughing hysterically.

Julya enters the building and is greeted by a couple of staff members. The custodian walks by and says, "Praise the Lord!"

She responds, "Hello, and praise the Lord to you, too!"

He says to her with a smile, "You should say hallelujah when I say 'Praise the Lord!'"

Julya responds, "Yeah, that's what the pastor says and I said praise the Lord to you and you responded with a correction to me! You're not even following your own instructions!"

As she walks through the sanctuary toward the administrative offices, she enters the building and into the office where her cubical flanks the corner of the building. She slides the mouse and the dialogue box appears requesting the user name and password. She clicks the "alt," "control," and "del" buttons on the keyboard and then enters the pastor's information to gain access. She begins her work but notices additional files are visible while in his profile but initially does not pay attention—she focused on the files that she works from in the familiar folders.

Scene: Pastor Danig is at home in his study
—R-rating for explicit language and content:

Pastor Danig is reading through his *Thompson Concordance* and going over scriptures in preparation for his words for the conference. He receives a call from one of the associate pastors who's also attending the conference.

"Praise the Lord, Pastor Danig! How are you?"

Pastor Danig: "I'm doing fine—just busy making preparations for the conference."

"Well," the associate pastor says, "yeah, you know you can't have all work and no play and so at the conference we do a few fun things to break up the monotony and sort of celebrate from having to do so much in ministry. You know people don't see all of the hard work that we do—we are behind the scenes helping people out, visiting hospitals, prisons and feeding the poor. We work really hard and I sometimes think it goes unappreciated—so sometimes we reward ourselves on these trips."

Pastor Danig responds, "Well, what do you mean? Are you guys going jet skiing or bowling or something between conference times?"

"We could but not exactly, I mean we could do those things too but we have an honors club where we have an oath not to share our private entertaining lifestyles with anyone."

Pastor Danig responds, "Well, I agree with you, I don't really want people peering into my personal lifestyle. I like a degree of privacy but that is a bit difficult when you're a pastor. You have to be transparent so the flock can see what you're doing and see you as a real person and not some iconic figure that has something to hide."

The assistant pastor responds, "That's what I'm talking about. People need to see you for the human that you are and you are entitled to have fun especially after you do so much good for everyone."

Pastor Danig interrupts, "Well, I'm not doing it for some type of reward from man. I think I'm blessed that I'm getting a salary to do God's work and I love searching and studying scriptures and sharing it with the congregation."

"Well, that's great that you're appreciating the salary part but in the pastoral honors society, we've made an oath to keep what stays in conferences to stay in conferences. No one needs to know that you can play around a little. It's our nature to want more than one woman. God put them on this planet—in fact there are more women on this planet than there are men and so what does that tell you? You shouldn't be sleeping with one woman for the rest of your life. In fact, there are woman out there that want a man on the side and I'm being real. I'm talking about married woman who wants to add you to their trophy that you gave them some sexual healing."

Pastor Danig has a shocked look on his face and then says, "You're listening to too much Marvin Gaye! Are you serious? I cannot believe that you're saying this! Anyway, I have a wife that I love and I am not going to cheat on her."

Associate pastor: "Well, that's what they all say. Your wife does not understand the things that you have to go through. You're putting your life on the line for people in the ministry and while you're out on the mission fields, it's okay to consent and do some things. Take a look a Solomon. How was it possible that he was able to have so many wives and concubines and still be blessed of the Lord with so much wisdom?"

Pastor Danig: "Come on, you know what the Bible says about adultery. You're trying to rewrite the Bible," the pastor responds. "Are you trying to say that I can have women on the side and still be blessed?"

Associate pastor: "Come on, take a good look. God doesn't need you to live a boring lifestyle and expect you to do all of these things in ministry."

Pastor Danig: "Oh, so now you have the mind of God?"

The associate pastor continues, "Look, our honors club has all of us hard-working pastors getting some on the side. It will even help you appreciate your wife."

Pastor Danig: "Why does the reward have to be sexual in nature?"

Deacon: "Just pay attention for a second! Your wife is someone you can come home to and the women that we deal with are not looking for a commitment nor are they looking to deal with you in the future. This honors club allows you to have a little fun with a consenting beautiful woman with no strings attached."

Pastor Danig: "This sounds like some Heidi Fleiss madness in the church!"

The associate pastor continues and laughs while saying, "Now don't you fall in love! These are some quality, professional woman and our honors club has already arranged—"

He interrupts. "This is some sort of Heidi Fleiss arrangement in the church and you're setting this ministry up for a big bust by the FBI! You mean to tell me that you guys have hired prostitutes?"

The associate pastor interrupts, "No, no, no…don't look at it like that! They are not prostitutes! These are career women who want a quality man on the side without any attachments some of them are married and they want to get it out of their systems! In fact, their husbands even know that they're doing this because they have an open relationship."

Pastor Danig: "Okay, I cannot believe what I'm hearing!"

The associate pastor interrupts, "That's what most of the new pastors say when they learn of this. You'll either come around or just live your boring stressful lifestyle as a pastor! You think about what I said and remember the honors club has an oath not to say anything and I know you'll do just that. You think about what I just said and go on and do what you are comfortable with."

The pastor then responds, "I cannot involve myself with this type of activity!"

"Well, let me tell you something, Mr. young rookie pastor, if you think you're living in a sanctified world, think again. No one is living right and that's why your Jesus died on the cross. People are doing wrong every day."

"What we do is have a little harmless fun and the good we do for so many people does not outweigh what some might consider as wrong. This is our personal business and consenting adults have agreed to do these things! The fun that we have does not do harm to anyone!"

Pastor Danig: "My Jesus? Isn't he your Jesus, too?"

The associate pastor says, "Do you know that if you think sinfully, it is the same as actually doing the act. Men think about have relations with some other chick all the time! I mean, admit it, we're always fantasizing about something and you, too—you're just too self-righteous to admit it. If some fine woman crossed your path, you might, in that fleeting moment, think of something sexual or covet her in some way even if you never engaged the person! Now if you're going to think it and the penalty is the same and if no good thing dwells in the flesh, why not just do it and ask forgiveness later? Again, you might be asking for forgiveness for something you might not have done wrong on—basically, just to cover all bases, just ask God to forgive you on a regular basis for sins of omission and commission."

Pastor Danig: "This is absolutely crazy, you know that Bible says, 'Should I continue in sin that grace may abound?' We shouldn't tempt God or act like we don't know any better. And let me tell you, I don't imagine having sex with another woman that I see and find attractive."

The associate pastor disagreed, "You're saying this but I want you to think about what you know about intimacy and having sex with a woman. When you see God's creation, you just say, oh, she's beautiful, and move on!" The associate pastor says, "I find that hard to believe! You might imagine her going down on you or a scene might flash through your mind that you're tappin' from behind!"

Pastor Danig, "Those are your thoughts and I really need to ask this question. Are you a pastor? Why are you talking like this?"

The associate pastor: "I'm being frank and I'm tired of the plastic preachers with these pious attitudes like they are above reproach. These pastors have these sex hormones inside of them to the point that they will have sex with anything, a woman, man or a dog for that matter."

Pastor Danig responds, "A dog? Okay, I've heard enough and you are out of line. You speak of venial sins and lasciviousness is on your tongue! I hope I don't see you at the conference because I'm going to have a few words with you and you're not going to like it! As for now I'm done with this!"

The associate pastor: "Well, Pastor, before you get off this phone, you'll find that the people in your company are all the same. When you go to the conference, just listen to the conversations, I mean, really listen and you'll see what I'm talking about. The people out there are talking ministry things and then conversations divert over the honor's club stuff. You'll know and you let me know when you're ready to have a little fun. You are new to all of this and don't even think about trying to blow the whistle! Just keep your mouth shut or you can still participate—it's up to you! Take a good look around you and notice how the ones who get caught and are in the media are the ones who stepped outside of our honors club. You can mess around safely and no one gets hurt, reputation and all. Good day, sir!"

Scene at church office:

As July is multitasking mode, she is working on the PowerPoint slide show with her cellphone plugged in the wall and earpiece in one ear. She gives instructions to her children, "I need you guys to put all of your dirty clothes in the hamper and when I get home all of your homework better be done. I'm going to check it."

The call-waiting light illuminates and she switches over to pastor Danig. When she answers he says, "Hey, Julya, did you ever get a chance to connect with the IT guy?"

She said, "No, I haven't heard from him yet."

Pastor Danig: "Okay, well, how's everything coming along?"

She says, "Things are going good, Pastor, and thanks for the login information. I'm getting things ready and should be finished in a couple of hours. I have some questions about your presentation but I can do most of the preliminary work with the slides before I ask you."

"Okay, well, that's good, just call me or send me an email of what you have and I'll make any changes if needed."

Scene: Pastor at home with wife:

Pastor Danig is sitting in the kitchen drinking hot chocolate and working on his laptop.

Maylee comes in the kitchen and asks, "Are you busy?"

He said, "No, go ahead, hun."

"Well, I thought about what the waitress said and I think I should get someone to watch the kids and go to the conference with you." Honey, I realize that I complain about us not spending time together and you're always away on some conference."

He interrupts, "No, honey, don't bother getting someone to watch the kids. Perhaps you can go on the next conference because I'll be in a work capacity that won't allow us to spend quality time."

She says, "I understand, honey, but it's just us being together on the plane ride and in the hotel between your conference stuff."

He says, "Well, it sounds nice and perhaps we can do it next time because I'm in a work capacity and really need time to myself so that I can concentrate and focus on the many presentations that I will be doing over the three-day period."

She says, "So you think me being there is going to distract you or be a hindrance to what you have to do? I think I can help you and even relieve some of the stress."

Pastor Danig: "Honey, that's what I don't want, I need to be focused and your distraction is a good one and not the type that I need on this trip. I'm new to this conference stuff and I need to acclimate myself to the way they do things. I'm looking at this like a business trip and I don't think husbands are bringing their wives on business trips."

She says, "I thought this was the church and I know they won't mind if you brought your wife. In fact, while you're going into the preparation stuff, I'll even leave if necessary to give you an opportunity to focus on what you're doing! I will also not attend any of the conference so you can have your space."

Pastor Danig: "Again, honey, I'm going to solo on this one!"

Maylee pauses and says, "Okay, you know I'm trying to do something to be involved with you and the ministry! I once heard someone tell me that family is so important and we should be careful about how we let our work, lifestyle, and the rat-race pull us away from our family. The months go by and during these sensitive times of our lives, we miss something. Perhaps your child needs you there when learning how to ride a bicycle.

He looks at her and says, "Honey, you don't think I realize this and I've been there for special moments like the ones you've said but…."

"Hold on, sweetie," she said, "you don't understand, you might realize this but your actions take you away and it is becoming more frequent. All I'm asking of you is when you go on this conference, I know that you are one of the keynote speakers but hear what I'm saying and pray that you don't turn a deaf ear on what I'm saying."

Pastor Danig said, "Okay, and I'm going to get this call—I will think on what you've said. I have three days to think about it, hun." He walks away and goes to the den.

Scene: Deacon's house:

The wife of the deacon is on the phone talking to one of her girlfriends about the issues of the church. She agrees with her husband and shares his sentiment with her friends.

"Girl, you know they're trying to get the members to support some fund-raising campaign where they're raising money for some research the city is trying to do for some property. Why does the church have to pay for some research on some land that they might not be able to build on anyway? So the church is going to get the members to give towards something that might result in them possibly not being able to build on it anyway. That's sounds pretty risky. Girl, why can't they get the city or someone else to do the research and wouldn't be easier for them to just find some land where money doesn't have to be spent on all this research? Yeah, I think it is some type of scheme for the city to get the church to pay for this stuff. They already know what the research shows, that's why no one has built on this land anyway. They want to get money out of the church and then someone else will benefit from the information that the land is sacred or has some fossils or environmental importance that might prevent anyone from building on it. So what's the outcome? Well, my husband tried to talk sense to the pastor about going to a place where there is already a building and work from there. Take the money you raise and make a warehouse or any building church-ready."

Scene: Day at the airport:

The pastor is going through the security check. He removes his Stacy Adams shoes and places them in the bin with his wallet. The security personnel asks him, "Please put your laptop and the iPad in separate bins."

He then walks through the scanner and Pastor Danig looks at the security person and asks, "Why are you staring at the genitals? You have this scanner that can see the entire body and you're focusing on the genital area!"

The security person said, "Sir, relax. There is no possible way for you to know what area of the scanner that I'm looking! I'm not looking at the genital area only. We have to make sure nothing dangerous is strapped on your body and that includes your scrotum."

Pastor Danig: "I cannot believe this! I'm a law-abiding, God-fearing man of God and this is a violation of my privacy! You need to chase after the real terrorists!"

Security person: "Sir, how would you feel if I didn't properly inspect you or anyone thoroughly for that matter? Now keep in mind that I've been thoroughly trained on these issues and feel insulted that you don't want to trust the system that is here to protect you and everyone that's boarding these planes. Now, imagine a real terrorist coming through and instead of testicles, he has grenades for testicles. Would you feel comfortable sitting next to a passenger that has grenades for balls, oh, I mean testicles?"

Pastor Danig: "How does someone get into an airport with grenades in their pants? Never mind...."

Scene: On plane in first-class section:

Pastor Danig is sitting First Class across from a CFO of an Information Technology business who is talking to the CEO on his Bluetooth device and typing on his laptop. Pastor Danig became interested in the conversation by the CFO as he listened to him discuss aspects of the business.

CFO: "Our third-quarter projections give a surprising 4-million-dollar profit and I'm imagining that we could save more by streamlining. I believe outsourcing to our India programmers would have made our profit close to $6.5 million. Our department shows intermediate to advanced programmers and the India market gives us the advanced programmers across the board. Our current team of programmers consistently met deadlines on the contracted projects but it is my recommendation to dissolve the web design department and outsource to meet the demands of the more than 50 contracted websites. We have ColdFusion as our platform in conjunction with Java and Visual Basic. We've utilized XML to bring about some fascinating things for our clients in the web pages."

Pastor Danig is amazed at how quickly this CFO is ready to shut down a department over the bottom-line issue. He pondered that so many people are going to be laid off because a company desires to outsource to the India market. It's all about the money. No one cares about who will suffer in these sweeping changes.

When the CFO finishes his conversation, he looked over at Pastor Danig and said, "Hello."

Pastor Danig: "How are you?"

CFO: "I'm fine, I'm sure you overheard some of what I was talking about and it's a tough world out there! I'm going to be the guy that has to break the news to our existing programmers that they we will no longer need their services and that we've found a more efficient and cost-effective way to make more money. We can simply get more of the contracted jobs done in a shorter period of time and with less overhead."

Pastor Danig: "How does this make you feel? I mean, it sounds like your firm is prospering with the loyal workers that you have and now because an opportunity arises where you can save some money and perhaps make more money—that leaves people without work who've worked hard to make your company the success that it shares now."

CFO: "Well, yes, they have been instrumental in the success of our company and I'm sure they realize that risk in the B2B environment. These programmers took the risk of working for private corporations and that's why we have contracts. The contracts let both parties know that upon completion we may no longer need their services."

Pastor Danig: "If you don't mind, you have more than 50 contracts and it sounds like you're letting your existing programmers go to simply make more money!"

CFO: "We have now found a way to meet the demands of our many contracts by outsourcing to our India friends. They are quite skilled in this arena and we can hire more of them to get this workload done in a shorter period of time. This business is cutthroat, I must admit, but we try to be as fair as possible with the contracts. The move to dissolve an entire department comes with a severance package that will give our programmers plenty of time to find other work. In fact, programmers make good money but they are a dime a dozen!"

Pastor Danig: "Wow, I'm shocked! So I'm imagining that the programmers in India are less expensive per hour than our American programmers. That's pretty clever and knowing something about the currency exchange, you probably want the programmers to stay in India and send you the scripting over the Internet."

CFO: "Quite right! You understand what we're doing."

Pastor Danig: "It sounds good for the company and for those in India because they will be working, but this is a classic example of how our system fails to support the people who live and work here!"

CFO: "And that's the job of a CFO—my only concern is the bottom line of the company. I have to put emotions aside and make decisions that are for the benefit of the company."

Pastor Danig: "It sounds so sterile! Your company is made up of people that you can easily get rid of for the simple means to make more money!"

Scene: Meeting with pastors—day before conference starts:

All five pastors sit in the lounge area of the hotel and discuss the order of the conference. The three-day conference involves music and keynote speakers. The discussion started with sidebar conversations and how things are going in each pastor's ministry. They started talking about marriage and the dynamics at the home-front.

The first pastor worked his voice in a way to sound deep. He started by asking the question, "How does your wife handle you being out of town doing God's work?"

Pastor Danig wanted to say something but paused to listen to the responses from the other pastors. They all had something negative to say about how their wives weren't supporting them in the ministry. It was the same story across the board about wives complaining about visitations and praying for the sick.

The first pastor continued by saying, "That's why we do the conferences, because it's work and play and it takes us away from hearing all of that! It is our way of being in a relaxing environment while we work. And don't bring your wife—that's a complete no-no!"

Pastor Danig thought to himself, "Hmmm, maybe it's a good thing that I didn't bring my wife on this one!" He then interjected and said, "So why wouldn't a pastor bring his wife?"

A pause occurred from everyone and silence for the span of five seconds and then one of the pastors jumped in and said, "For the very reasons they we've just talked about. We love our wives but we don't want them in our space all of the time."

Pastor Danig said, "I don't see how a wife attending a conference would be in our space all of the time! I see it as a form of support—the wife being there while you make preparations for what we do at these conferences. Aren't our wives our better halves? You guys will say this in the pulpit in a hot second but now there seems to be a lot of complaining!" One of the pastors jumps in and says, "I'm gathering that your wife is here!"

Chuckles from the other pastors could be heard.

Pastor Danig responded calmly, "No, she isn't here!"

Another pastor jumps in and says, "My point exactly, your wife isn't here and this is your second time at one of these conferences!"

Pastor Danig: "But I don't see the harm in it if she was here."

The first pastor says, "Okay, slow down for a second, Pastor Danig! We've all been working in ministries for years! Take it from us older and seasoned cats.

We know what it takes to preserve our marriage! It is a tough job doing ministry the way we do ministry! We know that your wife means well but she doesn't fully understand all that you do and she doesn't have to. There are certain things that a man needs in order to continue ticking in this business and yes, I said business. We work our tails off to change people's lives!" We are simply getting a little carte blanch treatment as a reward! We're going to have some fun while we do it and we're not going to let some philosophy prevent us from doing so."

Pastor Danig raised his eyebrow and said, "Philosophy? What about what the word of God says?"

Another pastor interjected with, "The word of God. Okay, Pastor Danig, enlighten us about what the word of God says!"

Pastor Danig: "Well, I shouldn't have to, pastors and ministers! You're all men who study and preach the word, so you know what it says. I think the problem sometimes is that we use the word selectively to suit our needs and we tend to not adhere to the things that bring about consequences on the stuff that we're doing and should not be doing."

"Another minister interjects, "Okay, rookie pastor, you'll learn after you've spent so many years trying to do good and it goes unappreciated that you're going to do whatever it takes to preserve your sanity and the relationships with the ones you love. People want help and why do we help people on a spiritual and physical level? Well, we do it because we're driven to do it! Now if the benefits that we enjoy in our honors club play into all of this, then why not? We should be able to enjoy some fun stuff, even if it's a little wild or crazy!"

Pastor Danig said, "I am determined to live a life that's pleasing to the Lord and will take no part in this honor's club activity."

"Well, no one is asking you to but it's there if you want to!"

Pastor Danig replied by saying, "I think what you're all doing is corrupt and dishonest. You really need to find other ways of having fun rather than getting involved with someone outside of your marriage!"

"Well, young pastor," replied one of the ministers, "some of our wives are in agreement with this arrangement and have no problem with it! They would rather us have a consenting encounter with someone they know will not yield an attachment than for us to get with someone they know nothing about and then later find out that their husband ran off with that person. These are things they don't have to worry about and since women know how men are, they do this to protect their marriages."

Pastor Danig: "All men aren't like that! That is a self-fulfilling prophecy!"

The other minister continued, "They know we want to creep and so they've given us the green light to get it out of our systems! Trust me, it strengthens the marriage and takes the wondering out of the equation!"

Pastor Danig: "How can you speak of trust when you doing untrustworthy things against your marriage?"

The minister continues, "Trust me; you'll see that it is better this way!"

Pastor Danig was perturbed and said, "I think you have the wrong approach and I won't take part in this!"

The other minister replied, "Okay, Pastor Danig, it sounds like you're crossing the line with this because some of our wives are in agreement with this arrangement! You've just been given an opportunity to try something that might preserve your marriage and it is an option, so let's drop this and move on with the business at hand."

Scene: The next day and Julya's plane lands in Dallas-Fort Worth:

Julya hurries through the airport with her carryon baggage and her laptop. She reads the sign for the shuttle that takes passengers to the hotel. Upon her arrival, she tells the front desk her name and they give her the key card to her room. The maître d gives her an envelope and helps her with her luggage to the room. When she arrives in the room, there is a message on the hotel phone which says to meet with the pastor and other staff in the lounge at 7:30 A.M. sharp in the hotel dining area. Julya is amazed at the service that she's receiving at the 5-star hotel environment. She looks around the room with a bit of surprise noticing all of the conveniences. There's a mini refrigerator, microwave and a flat-screen TV in the bedroom portion and the living area.

Julya presses the speed dial for her mom on her cellphone. "Hey, Mom, I'm calling you again and just wanted to let you know that I finally got checked in and I'm in the room! Mom, you wouldn't believe it but this suite that they have me in looks like something for a couple on a honeymoon! I didn't realize that business trips would give this level of hotel accommodations for the workers. I mean, there's so much stuff in the room, that I don't even need to leave because they gave me per diem and I get room service—so I can work in the room without being disturbed."

Her mom quietly replies, "It sounds really nice. I'm wondering why they would put you in such a fancy suite like this when you can do your work in a regular room."

Julya says, "I don't know, Mom, but it really helps me to work better when I'm in such a nice environment. They're treating me like a professional and I really like this."

Mom says, "Well, sweetie, I hope you get your work done and that you're not distracted by all of that fancy stuff!"

Julya: "Okay, Mom, well, I must go and I will call you later!"

Mom: "Okay, sweetie, talk to you later."

Scene: Musicians are in conference room rehearsing:

While the musicians are setting up and tuning the instruments, conversations about the sound are being heard. The sound engineer is asking each musician questions as to what they want in their floor monitors. While the sound engineer is setting up the sound, the drummer and the keyboardist are having a conversation about the administrative assistant. The drummer says, "So have you seen the new administrative assistant?"

The keyboardist replied by saying, "Yes, I went in to pick up my check and saw her in a meeting with the pastor."

Drummer, "Yeah, man, is she married, because she looks real good, man?"

Keyboardist: "I don't think she's married but I think she got all that baby daddy drama going on! I think she has two children and that dude ain't doing right by those children! He just pops in on her in on her when he wants to hit it and he always manages to hit that when comes around with a little money. She's a nice girl and I don't think she put him in the system for the child support stuff. He needs to pay some type of child support for those kids instead of just giving her money here and there! I heard this cat is still living home and always hanging with young cats that want him around because he's able to get drinks."

Drummer: "Oh, okay, so are they serious?"

Keyboardist: "No, they aren't serious, like I said she's just trying to be nice to this dude because of those kids but he's not about anything. He's a player, man, and she needs to be careful because he might get her pregnant again!"

Drummer: "Well, she has two children—are both children his children?"

Keyboardist: "Nope. Her first child was from her uncle. The story was that he was messing around with her for years and when she got pregnant she didn't want anyone to know because she knew that someone would try to shoot this guy if they found out! She told everybody that her current dude was the father but I don't think he's the father of either one of those kids. They look nothing like him but that would come out if she had a DNA test."

Drummer: "Man, this sounds like some *Maury Povich Show* mess! Man, that's crazy, dude. This girl has problems, and how do you know all of this stuff?"

"Well, she's my cousin's best friend and my cousin actually helped her get the church administrative job. But let me tell you, don't share what I've told you! It could be a rumor but—"

The drummer interrupts, "Man, I want to get to know this girl!"

Keyboardist: "Why, you don't even know her and I think there's too much drama with her situation and man, don't be acting crazy because you're liking the way she looks. Some of them pretty girls come with some major issues."

Drummer: "I think we all have issues and I just need to get to know her because she seems like a nice girl."

Keyboardist: "Well, you're saying that by looking at her from a distance but if you want to take that chance, you might get a chance to meet her because I think she's working at the conference."

Drummer: "Are you serious—man, I got to find out where she is because I want to try to holla at that!"

Keyboardist: "Man, you're crazy! You're a sucker for a pretty face!"

Drummer: "Well, let me find out what she's all about and I'll go from there! It won't help to find out now, will it?"

Keyboardist: "Slow your roll, partner, she's here in a work capacity and you might not see her. She's hanging out with the uppity pastor's entourage and if you're lucky you might get to say a quick hello to her. She's in the company where people are watching all the time. I think this is her first conference and she's not going to come here acting crazy."

Drummer: "Man, what are you talking about? The people over here aren't just doing conference stuff! These wild-ass pastors check out the woman and people are sneaking into hotel rooms and doing wild shit!"

Keyboardist: "Are you kidding? Again, if you're basing what other people are doing, you need to slow your roll because she will most likely shut you down."

Drummer: "Hey, I'm going to find out for myself and I'll show you how it's done."

Keyboardist: "Okay, well, you do that, now let's get a couple of songs going for this sound check."

The keyboardist begins playing gospel chop runs during his warmup. The drummer is standing over him and admiring the runs and asks him, "Hey, man, can you show me those runs?"

The keyboardist starts playing chords and tells the drummer, "I invented these cluster chords!"

The Guitarist said, "That ain't nuthin' but clutter chords. Man, what are you playing?"

The drummer disagreed and said, "What are you talking about, that is tight!"

Guitarist: "Uh, uh, I need to hear the chords! That's too many notes! Who understands that? He's pressing too many notes at one time."

Keyboardist: "Did you see the bass player?"

Drummer: "Yeah, he's right there in the sound booth."

Keyboardist, "Fellas, how close are we? We need to get a sound check going so these guys can get the levels right. I need someone to get on the mic so we can do a sound check with the band and the vocals."

Scene: Meeting with pastor, administrative assistant and two staff members:

Pastor Danig thanks everyone for meeting with everyone and opens up the meeting with a prayer. Pastor Danig and Julya have their laptops opened and begin discusses adjustments to the slides.

Pastor: "Okay, Julya, I would like to add this movie file to the PowerPoint as part of the presentation. The Lord has given me a change in my presentation and mini sermon. I'll send you the link to this file and you can add it to the twelfth slide."

As the pastor worked with Julya, he noticed that she was very fair and thought, "How did this woman get mixed up with a shiftless dude?" He then redirected his attention to the program and said, "Okay, they've given me 20 minutes to speak on tithing. This is going to be interesting because my approach is different from what they probably want to hear but I'm going to enjoy speaking on this one."

The pastor's fleeting thought of an admiration to his administrative assistant brought him to a place of where he needed to pray. In his silent prayer he asked God to remove thoughts of lasciviousness and one of covetousness. "Lord, my flesh is weak and I don't want my desires to take precedence over the desires you've placed in me for your good."

The meeting was short and so everyone closed their laptops and began ordering breakfast from the waiter.

Julya asked the question, "Should we tell the waiter to make separate receipts?"

Pastor Danig said, "Oh, no, on this trip you can use your per diem outside of what we'll cover and all of your meals are covered. If you decided to go to the spa and gift shop, that is your choice in the matter. You're working and this comes with the travel package. Anyway, order whatever you'd like."

Julya thought to herself, "This is nice! I never a business trip would cover all of these expenses! I'm not even coming out of pocket!"

Scene: Pastor Danig in his suite and the chain of events causes him to revise his presentation. The pastors are all meeting for dinner in the evening to finalize things such as what portion of tithing and giving will be taught:

Pastor Danig decided to pull out his research on the history of tithing and he felt that some ministries were teaching on tithing and giving in a manner that was not consistent with the word. He delved deeper and spent hours in his room researching online and making phone calls to some of the fathers in the ministry on tithing. He wanted to hear and see the different perspectives so that his comfort level would be validated. In his mind he knew that he was going against the grain because it would move in a direction of basically telling people not to give and this conference was really about raising money.

"We need to get people to be willing to give and we want to show them in scripture that giving is something good when done toward a Godly cause. We are men of God and we will use the scriptures to get people to realize that they will be blessed if they sow seeds into this and associate ministries."

Pastor Danig stayed in his room for hours because as he researched, he found some interesting and enlightening information on tithing and found himself stuck in the book of Galatians. He found that tithing seemed like a principle that was being forced upon people and that they were made to feel guilty if they didn't tithe ten percent of their first fruits. He felt a surge of guilt because he pressured some members to give when they really didn't have it to give. In his conviction, he felt that he needed to give back by letting people know in any platform that he was on that no one should ever feel pressured into giving. This includes people who have and those who don't—the giving should be something natural and the willingness should come from the individual without the pressure of innuendoes and trickery schemes from pulpits across the world.

Scene: First day at conference:

Pastor Danig sits with the other pastors on the panel and he is scheduled to speak on the second day of the conference. The music begins and the praise team ushers in worship with an awesome musical presentation. The crowd is standing and clapping their hands in all of the excitement. The pastor who is scheduled to speak stands in front of the pulpit as the praise team concludes a song. He stands in front of the pulpit with a deep disposition and is making adjustments at the pulpit. He's arranging the Bible and towel and a hand clock to monitor his time. He then adjusts the podium mic to his level and begins to sing along with the praise team as they begin ending the song. The organist picks up as the praise team exits the stage and the pastor continues singing along with the organ. The organist can be seen adjusting the draw-bars and making it sound real churchy in the conference room. While the pastor is singing, the people in the audience acknowledge what he says with "Amens" and "Sing, Pastor" and "Yes, yes, yes." A woman is seen jumping up and down with her hands folded around herself as if she is hugging herself. The pastor then concludes the song and begins speaking with a deep and provocative sounding voice.

Pastor: "Can we all stand and give God a hallelujah praise? Come on and put those hands together and give God the highest praise! You're not clapping your hands for me but you're giving God the highest praise." He pauses while the musician clicks the button on the organ to get the Leslie cabinet to spin and begins playing chords that fill the building. "Come on and get your break-through because your victory is in your praise. Praise God for what he's done in your life and praise him for what he's yet going to do in your life. Come on and praise him!"

The crowd gets louder and the organist pulls out the draw-boards and works the Leslie switch, causing the organ sound to permeate the room. People start moving into the aisles and you can hear some people praising God and some speaking in tongues.

The pastor says, "Come on and praise him until you get your break-through! Don't worry about who's around you and who you think is looking at you! Don't let anyone distract you from your praise! Don't let the devil steal your joy and your blessing. Go ahead and praise him! You're in the right place where the saints of God can give God some praise." The pastor yells into the mic in a way that creates distortion, "Hallelujaaaaaaah! Praise him and praise him some more."

The music escalates as the volume of the praise escalates. People are jumping around and shouting and dancing. The music now involves the entire band. The sound of the bass and guitar are added as the musicians play additional runs to enhance the music. The keyboardist starts accenting around what the organist is doing. The music now takes a change and moves toward a rhythmic pattern of a shouting beat. The drummer starts it off and the pulse of the music has most of the people clapping and dancing to a shouting beat. The musicians begin getting creative by adding interesting changes and patterns to the shouting music. You could hear interesting gospel changes and incorporating musical themes from game shows and sound tracks to movies. The crowd is captivated in the music and most don't even understanding the changes in the music but simply moving to the beat of the drums.

The shouting continues for about three minutes and then the pastor gives a signal to wind it down with, "Yesssssssssss, yeaaaaaahhssssss, yeeeeehhhh eeehhhhh eehhhhhhsssss, yeeaahhhhhssssssss, yesssss, Lord, yeahssss, Lord….." He repeats this and then starts talking to the people. "You may take your seats if you can. Isn't God worthy? Can you feel his presence? Now I'd like to thank all of you for attending this conference and I know that your lives will not be the same at the close of this conference. You are going to be blessed beyond anything you might have imagined because you are here not by your own volition but because God ordained this moment in your life. I want you to know that there is a word for you today and pray that the word impacts your life. Now, they've only given me 20 minutes to minister to all of you and I think my time starts now. I promise. I won't be before you for long because we have some awesome speakers that you will get a chance to hear over the next three days. I want to also acknowledge our praise team for the wonderful work they do and how they ushered in the praise. I know that God is our audience and our goal should be to simply please God. Did you know that God inhabits the praises of his people? Now if you would turn your Bibles to a familiar scripture in Malachi 3, verse 7. Say amen if you have it."

Spurious acknowledgements such as an "Amen" and "Yes" sound throughout the room.

He then waits a few more seconds and begins reading the scripture. He charismatically exhorts, "Read along silently as I read aloud! 'Even from the days of your fathers, ye are gone away from mine ordinances, and have not kept them. Return unto me, and I will return unto you, saith the Lord of hosts. But ye said, wherein shall we return? Will a man rob God? Yet ye have robbed me. But ye say, wherein have we robbed thee? In tithes and offerings. Ye are cursed with a curse: for ye have robbed me, even this whole nation. Bring ye all the tithes into the storehouse….'" He then braces the podium and says, "Now before we begin our look at these passages of scripture in Malachi, let us understand that we do live in the grace period and this notion of giving in the church is something that has brought about controversy in Christendom.

I want you all to see how this scripture can be applied to your life in terms of giving but before we do this, let's take a look at what's happening in this scripture. Let's also realize that the scriptures from the Old Testament will be fulfilled in our lives even though we are living in the New Testament."

Scene in conference room:

Pastor Danig speaks on tithing. He stands at the podium and calls one of the praise team members to sing a brief solo of a song entitled "I Give It All to You."

Pastor Danig: "Can you please turn to Proverbs 3:9 and read with me? I'm reading from the King James Version. And it reads, 'Honor the Lord with substance, and with the first fruits of all thine increase.' Now please turn with me to Deuteronomy the 14th chapter and the 22nd verse. Let's read, 'Thou shalt truly tithe all the increase of thy seed, that the field bringeth forth year by year.' Verse 23: 'And thou shalt eat before the Lord thy God, in the place which he shall choose to a place in his name there, the tithe of thy corn, of thy wine, and of thine oil, and the firstlings of thy herds and of thy flocks, that thou mayest learn to fear the Lord thy God always. And if the way be too long for thee, so that thou art not able to carry it, or if the place to be too far from thee, which the Lord thy God shall choose to set his name there, when the Lord thy God hath blessed thee: Then shalt thou turn it into money and bind up the money in thine hand, and shalt go unto the place which the Lord thy God shall choose: And thou shalt bestow that money for whatsoever thy soul lustiest after, for oxen, or for sheep, or for wine, or for strong drink, or for whatsoever thy soul desireth: and thou shalt eat there before the Lord thy God and thou shalt rejoice, thou and thine household, And the Levite that is within thy gates; thou shalt not forsake him, for he hath no part nor inheritance with thee. At the end of three years thou shalt bring forth all the tithe of thine increase the same year, and shalt lay it up within thy gates.' Before we take a closer look at this scripture, let's take a look at what the book of Deuteronomy and then we can look at the context of the scripture and the activities of the people during that dispensation of time." Pastor Danig refutes what the pastor preached about on the previous day and now the platform was no longer one of getting people to tithe but to give according to an increase. He gave the historical significance of the tithe and how it was used under the law. He then emphasized, "We are not under the law and need to change the way we give! We should not be giving under necessity or with the expectation that we're going to get something in return. The Bible speaks of giving on an increase and not with what God promised you. No one should be taking tithing off of their income. That isn't an increase, it is income that you need for your family to survive in this world that we live! An increase is something above and beyond what God promised you. No person in this congregation should be tithing off of their income and then having to come to a church or some nonprofit organization for help. This is the problem in our churches. We place guilt on the members to give when they are unable to give. We put pressure on people to give and then have them go home wondering how they are going to pay a bill with the money they put into an offering basket. This is not what God wants and He does not need your money. Ministries need to take a closer look at how they get money from its members. The church is not a club or a for-profit organization that needs to get money from people to do grand things like build fancy structures while people are struggling at home to make ends meet. The church is not an entity that should take from the poor and look good and then tell the members that they are not a lending institution when a person asks for help. We need to take a closer look at the scriptures and realize what God is trying to do in our lives. We do not need to come to conferences and give money and think that God is going to bless us because we gave to some ministry that purports to do the work of God. It is a shame. This message might not be popular amongst my distinguished colleagues but I didn't come here to be popular and God has given me a message for all of you. If you are able to give, do not give under duress or of necessity. Change your attitudes about giving. Don't give with the intent that you're going to get some sort of increase. If you are already blessed, then you should give with that attitude. I am blessed and I have an increase and I'm going to be a blessing with such an increase. Thank you and may God bless you all."

The people began clapping and then the pastor went to his seat and bowed his head to prayer as the minister in charge started the alter-call. The associate ministers were leaning over talking to each other in disagreement with Pastor Danig's approach and one of the ministers took out his smartphone and began typing a text message to the other pastors to schedule a meeting at the end of today's conference in the hotel lounge.

Scene in hotel lobby:

Pastor Danig is walking down the hotel area where books and CDs are being sold. He sees Julya and approaches her and says, "Thank you for the work you did! The presentation was controversial but it went according to the plans and the slide show fit nicely into the presentation. Thanks again."

Julya responds by saying, "You're welcome and is there anything else you'd like me to do?"

He said, "Actually, you've done all you needed to do for this conference and your support to me on my presentation was all that was needed. You are actually done and you should enjoy the rest of the time—consider it like a mini vacation."

She smiled and said, "Thank you but if you need me to do anything you know where to find me!"

Pastor Danig thought to himself, "Is she flirting with me or is she simply showing appreciation to the fact that she now has all of this free time? Is she feeling guilty and has a desire to continue working?" Danig replied by saying, "Well, I doubt that I'll need you for anything but feel free to contact me if you need anything."

She smiled and walked away.

As she made her way back to her room she encountered the drummer, who said, "Hello, are you the lady who works in the administrative office?"

She said, "Yes!"

Drummer: "I thought you looked familiar and I just wanted to say that my name is Douglas and I'm the drummer."

She said, "Yes, I know, I've seen you and I also get to see your time sheets every week."

Douglas responds, "Oh, so you signing checks now," and she said, "No, I only push the paper to get time sheets signed and filed properly so that when we are audited, everything is in order. It's just one of the many things that I do. Anyway, I must be going, I'm heading back to get some rest as I was up all night working on the pastor's presentation. I wanted it to be right; it's the perfectionist in me."

Douglas said, "Hold on before you rush off! I never did get your name!"

Julya: "Oh, I'm sorry, I'm Julya," and they shook hands and she started walking towards the elevators.

Douglas said as she was walking away, "So after you get your rest, would you like to do dinner later?"

She said, "Are you asking me out to dinner? You don't even know me and I don't know you!"

Douglas responded, "That's the purpose of going out to dinner! Well, if you're available to talk. I don't want to push this issue if you're uncomfortable. I think we are both here on a work capacity."

Julya then said, "I don't want to pass judgment but I'm leery of musicians! They seem to be players and I don't have time for that! I don't want to open up any doors to any more drama."

Douglas replied, "I don't think it's fair for you to categorize musicians this way but if you feel we're that way, I think dinner might clear up that misconception. In fact, I will guarantee that you are wrong about your generalization about musicians! If you're wrong about us musicians, you would have completely shut down an opportunity to be friends with someone who might be the total opposite of what you think."

She then said, "Okay, if I decide to do dinner with you and don't sleep through the night, I'll be at the Smorgasbord Diner at around 8:00 P.M."

Douglas: "Okay, that's fair enough and I'll see you there!"

Julya: "You might," and hurried into her elevator.

Scene: In restaurant:

It's 8:00 P.M. and Douglas has made his way to the Smorgasbord Diner, which is an upscale restaurant in the hotel.

The waiter asks, "For one?"

Then Douglas says, "No, can I get a table for two?"

Waiter: "Step this way, sir," and takes him to a table next to a window that overlooks a manmade lake. The restaurant has a romantic appeal as the lighting has the intensity of candles and the lake can be seen through the windowpane.

Douglas waits and waits and no Julya. In the distance the pastors from the conference can be seen sitting several tables down. They seem to be in a debate over scriptures but their volume is low. It is nearly 9:20 P.M. and Julya has not arrived.

The waiter suggests, "I can start you off with a drink if you'd like."

He responds, "Yes, I'd like a strawberry daiquiri."

When the waiter returns with the drink, Douglas begins sipping on the drink and looking at his phone through the messages and begins reading the message from the keyboardist. "Band members, we're going to meet at 7:30 A.M. to go over the songs. Please respond and let me know that you can make this earlier time as it is not on your agendas."

As he began texting, Julya walks up and asks, "Is this seat taken?" and Douglas responds, "It's reserved for you only." As she takes her seat, he finishes the text and taps send.

She looks at him and he responds, "Oh, I was sending a text to our music director, who conveniently scheduled for the musicians to meet tomorrow for an earlier rehearsal."

Julya responded, "Thank you for that bit of information but you didn't need to explain nor was I interested in knowing what you were doing on your phone."

Douglas said, "Okay, well, I'm glad you made it. I thought I'd be drinking this daiquiri all by myself!"

Scene: Pastors are at table debriefing on the presentations:

"Well, Pastor Danig, I thought your presentation was interesting and if I'm not mistaken, it seemed as though you were refuting or attacking the material that I taught yesterday," said one of the associate ministers. "In fact, you started off with the same scriptures that I used and then you segued into Galatians.

We need to be on one accord as it relates to the way we present this material. We don't need to operate in opposition to each other because there are those in the audience who will detect this dynamic."

Pastor Danig responds with a perturbed look on his face, "Hold on one second! Being on one accord is one thing and I think that if we're talking about giving or tithing, some of the same scriptures can be used. Now you mentioned that the audience can pick up on the dynamics of us being on one accord but you seem to have a problem with what I said and you showed it onstage. Now people see this!"

Minister: "Okay, Pastor Danig, what are you talking about? How do you know what I'm thinking by looking at me?"

Pastor Danig: "Well, I could see your response when I looked over at all of you and it certainly wasn't one of affirmation. No 'Amens' from you, in fact you nodded your head in opposition to what I said. Oh, yeah, it was apparent! I don't want to argue this point further and as I said, I came from the word of God. It is not always comfortable and simply because my approach was in opposition to what you taught on yesterday, you want to have an issue with me. I think it will be civil of us to agree to disagree and not debate in this public facility. If what I'm saying is against the word of God then I must apologize, but if what was said was from the Lord and this is what I believe, then I feel comfortable standing my ground. It is no disrespect to you but God's word will not return void. Our interpretation of the word is the reason why we're having this debate and I must be careful not to be isogetical. The very existence of so many religious views and denominations is the reason why we're having this problem anyway. There are many things we can do to maintain a notion of civility during this conference as we all have research skills and resources to help us understand the scriptures."

Minister: "Well, Pastor Danig, I realize what your stance is related to tithing. It opposes what we've been teaching for years at this conference. You literally told them to not give."

Pastor Danig interrupts, "Now that isn't true! Were you listening?"

Minister: "Oh, yes, I was listening!"

Another pastor interrupted, "Hold on and let me say this, after Pastor Danig spoke and the offering we took was this highest that we've taken in one night without any special offerings and lining people up and urging one hundred people to stand and give a set amount. So his approach was different but it came from the scriptures. The word reached someone and I think we need to look at it from the perspective of God's word. We have to understand it and apply it to our lives."

As the other pastor spoke, Pastor Danig noticed Julya on the far end of the restaurant sitting with the drummer and it caught his attention because he knew of her situation and she knew the drummer had some issues of his own. He kept looking over to see how they were interacting as the pastor continued in his defense. The other pastor asked him a question and he did not respond.

He then said, "Earth to Pastor Danig!"

The other pastors chuckled.

Pastor Danig said, "Well, I'm sorry, my mind went elsewhere for a minute."

Minister: "Well, don't stress, Pastor Danig, and don't let the stress of it all get you discombobulated—we have these debriefs all the time and some-times they can be intense and so we're all here to defuse things when it appears to escalate." The minister then said, "Okay, gentlemen, we have one more day for the conference and so have any of you gotten a chance to relax? The golf course is calling my name and I think we can put that on the agenda for to-morrow because our keynote speaker is going to handle the last day of the conference and we are not required to stay for the concert that follows his presentation. It seems that we'll be free from duty by noon. So what time does the concert start?"

"Oh, it begins at 6 P.M. and as your agendas show the teachers in the mini-stry will be holding the break-out sessions until 3:00 P.M. So enjoy yourselves as our flights don't leave until Sunday morning."

Scene: Meeting has ended and Pastor Danig decides to walk in the direction of where Douglas and Julya are sitting on his way back to his room:

Pastor Danig: "Hello, Julya and Douglas, how are you all doing this evening?"

They both say, "Fine," at the same time.

"Well, I hope you guys enjoy the evening!" He proceeds out of the res-taurant.

Julya looks at him as he walks away and Douglas said, "Is there something wrong?"

Julya replied, "No, I just feel a little weird being here in a work capacity and the pastor sees me hanging out with someone I don't even know in some sort of romantic setting. This seems weird to me."

Douglas: "Well, I think you're overreacting a bit. We're just here having dinner and if you really want to know the truth in these matters, these so-called pastors and staff people are out here doing some things that they don't have any business doing! So don't feel guilty with our little innocent dinner!"

Julya: "What do you mean?"

"Well, people are in rooms doing business and pleasure, if you know what I mean."

She said, "Well, actually, I don't know what you mean! I thought this was a church event and that people on these conventions were doing God's work."

"Well, yes, they're doing God's work and they're also putting work in!"

Julya: "Putting work in? What? So you're saying that this dinner date that we're having is a prerequisite to you trying to put work in?"

Douglas: "No, that's not it, I'm just saying that you're feeling guilty about something sexual that did not happen between us and these guys are out there acting crazy when they know they're married or in committed relationships!"

Julya: "Why did you ask me to this dinner date?"

Douglas: "I thought you were very attractive and I wanted to get to know you."

Julya: "So you're looking at an outward appearance, you don't even know me!"

Douglas: "Well, then since we're on the topic of getting to know each other, why don't you tell me something about yourself."

Julya: "What makes you think I need to tell you something about myself? I don't know you well enough to tell you anything about myself."

Douglas: "Okay, let's just order dinner and see how the conversations go rather than sit here and stress out or act like we're interviewing each other. In this day and age, people really are interviewing each other. Everybody's trying to play these little games but in reality, when you ask someone what do they do for a living or what was your worst or best experience on a date, you're trying to find out something about that person."

Julya: "I'm going to tell you something about myself and then it will be your turn. Well, I'm a single mom and I have one boy who's four and a girl who's eight. I have my associate's degree and work at the church doing administrative work."

Douglas exclaims, "So do you have a significant other in your life?"

"I have a baby's daddy, if you really want to know, and I don't consider him a significant other. So tell me something about yourself."

Douglas: "Well, I work as a customer service representative in card services at American Express and I'm a part-time musician. I play the drums but I also have a mini-studio at home where I make beats. I have a six-year-old son but he lives with his mother and we don't get along. I'm trying to do right by my son but she has issues with me because we aren't together. So it's really about business when it comes to her and when I say business, I'm talking about paying child support and being able to visit. I think the real problem I'm having is that she controls how I get to see my son and I haven't gone to court to try to work this out. Do you allow your baby's daddy to see his children?"

Julya: "I wouldn't hold them from actually seeing their father but when he comes around, he brings his ghetto woman and he acts ignorant around the children with liquor on his breath sometimes or reeking of weed. I don't want my kids around that type of ignorance because I want them to grow up in a decent environment."

Douglas: "I don't mean to judge but how did you get mixed up with some dude that seems to be into drugs and whatnot?"

Julya: "Well, it's the environment we both grew up in and I used to be immature and a little wild but after my children were born, I quickly realized that that lifestyle is not for me. I don't want my children to grow up around a bunch of ignorance. I mean people wasting time hanging out drinking, smoking weed, having dazed sex and playing dominoes. These guys do these odd jobs to make money and I think my baby's daddy might be selling drugs. If he is, he's going to get caught and end up in jail. I'll then have a baby's daddy that's in jail and I don't even want to think about anything like that."

Douglas murmurs, "Well, it sounds like you still care about the dude and if he were to get his life in order, you guys sound like you could have a good thing because you share two kids together."

Julya responds with hesitation, "I don't think that's going to work out because he's immature and determined to hang with his homies. It is ridiculous. He doesn't want to change and I'm working and in school trying to raise the kids and it seems like I'm doing it by myself. So, what are you doing to try to be there for your son? You know, it sounds like we're both saying something about our baby and it almost sounds like we're the innocent victims in all of this. I don't think it's true. I think we all played a part in where we are now and now we expect things to go our way. In my mind, I thought he was the man for me and I had that mentality that he would be in my life if we had a child together. Maybe we would grow up together and eventually get married. I was delusional and maybe the weed I used to smoke or the drinking had something to do with me making such irrational decisions. I love my kids but I'm not going to fool myself into thinking that the way I did stuff in the past doesn't have an impact. I want what's best for my kids and I do pray that my baby's daddy gets saved and stops the lifestyle he's living."

Douglas: "Okay, that's interesting and you are hopeful for the best for him. I think that's cool and that dude don't know what he got. You are a good lady and I wish my baby's momma had that attitude. That's the thing that bugs me the most. When a woman plays games and uses the children to try to get me to do something. This woman already has me in the system for child support and those people get my money every month. I went through hell with the child support stuff because there was a court order for me to pay a certain amount every month and it was all about business. I felt that I did that and I gave them money when they needed extra. I don't get it. I think she's giving the money to her boyfriend and her family because they're always asking her for money and she seems to have it to give. It ticks me off because I'm stigmatized at my job for this child support stuff and I'm paying. She tries to make me appear to be a shiftless or deadbeat dad and I know that's not true. She's really angry because things didn't work out between us and I know she doesn't like this dude she's with because he has nothing to offer her. She does more for him than she ever did for me when we were dating and I've finally realized that it must be something going on in the bedroom why she's so sprung on this dude. She's going to realize that the sex will only take you but so far. Too many women get turned out with the sex. They want sex and the money and men are under pressure to do all these things to please a woman and—"

Julya interrupts, "What are you talking about? That makes no sense whatsoever! The dick! Do you really think that a woman behaves because of a dick?"

Douglas responds with a confident smile, "Absolutely! If you didn't have anything else going on outside of some toys, you would go to that shiftless father for some dick just to get your freak on! You might even do it just to get something out of him."

Julya responds with a disturbed look on her face, "You don't know what you're talking about!"

Douglas continues to smile, "Why the hostility? It looks like I struck a nerve. I know I'm telling the truth because I've seen it happen too many times."

Julya pauses and continues to listen to Douglas' reaction.

"Let me ask you a question. Did you ever use your sexual prowess to get something out of your baby's daddy?"

Julya pauses and says harshly, "No!"

Douglas laughs and says, "I find that hard to believe. Woman can be conniving and manipulate men with their sexual prowess. They do their hair a certain way, they put the perfume on, and they walk and shake the booty a certain way just to get a man's attention. They are slick with the eye contact and raising eyebrows and staring at the crotch area. They go for the men who appear to be successful because of the car they drive or the suit they wear. They try to pretend that their intent is subtle but they are out there trying to get with someone that might make their lifestyle a little better. I've seen it over and over again, if it ain't the sex, then it's the material thing. A woman knows how to find the man who has something material going on and men want to compete by having nice things so they can show it off to women. Men don't care that another man sees him in a cool car or suit unless he happens to have an attraction to another man but in this case, he gets nice things to impress a woman because he knows there are woman out there that gravitate to that. These pastors you see out here seem to have things and that's why you always see woman sitting in the front. They want to be with a man that's preaching the word of God because they believe that he's upright and trying to do the right thing. I don't think you understand but that's why so many pastors are in trouble because women are throwing themselves at these pastors and the temptation is so great that many of them end up getting in trouble. Haven't you noticed? All of these pastors at these conferences with the exception of one are married and not one of them brought their wives! This isn't some business trip that excludes wives. About ten years ago these pastors used to bring their wives and now all of a sudden these men need time away from their wives to strengthen their marriages. That's a bunch of mess. They're strengthening their marriages by playing on the side. They realize the type of woman they're involved with and it makes them appreciate their wives. It's absolutely insane some of the stuff you hear about at these conferences and I've been to a few. The playing is at every level. I mean from the musicians to the pastors and I'm going to tell it like it is. I got some of my play time in as well and I don't mean playing the drums. I had more sex at these conferences than I doing any other part of the year. The girls meet us dudes in the lobby and at the pool and we just hook up. Now since you don't seem to be interested in me as a friend because I can tell by your body language and some of the things you said about your baby's daddy, I'm not holding back from telling it like it is. I am here to play. I wanted you to come to this dinner so I can possibly hook up with you and eventually have sex. And since we're on the fleshly topic, you have a big booty that I'd love to see. Now if you're offended I'm sorry."

Julya stood with an astonished look on her face, "I cannot believe what you just said and I am disgusted!"

Douglas: "Well, many think it and I'm guilty for saying it."

Julya: "Waiter, can I get the check for my order, please?"

Waiter: "Certainly, madam."

Douglas interrupts: "I'll take the check—don't worry about it."

Julya: "No, I'm paying for my own, I don't need no overly sexed musician paying for my dinner and I'm not the type where you can buy me something and I'm sleeping with you. It ain't going down like that!" Julya slams $40 on the table and says, "That should handle my order plus the tip," and she walks off. She is utterly upset and says to herself, "I cannot believe I succumbed to this dinner date, which has really showed me how doggish men really are! The only thing I got out of this was that I realize more than ever that men are corrupt and I hope that one day God will bless me with a real man who's not out there looking for a woman he can take advantage of."

Douglas sits at the table and wonders to himself, "I should have kept my mouth shut. Maybe it was the daiquiri…." He grabs his cellphone and calls the keyboardist. "Hey, man, I went on a dinner date with Julya."

Keyboardist (Amos): "Well, how did it go?"

"Well, she paid for both of our meals."

Amos: "Really, why did you let her pay for both of your meals?"

Douglas: "It's the pimp in me, I manage to get women to do for me and I don't care how because I've been played all my life. I'm just returning the favor. I knew that Julya wasn't my type and I knew she wasn't really interested in going further with anything so I did what I had to do to get something out of her."

Amos: "You sound crazy. So getting her to pay for your meal was all you could do? You're not a pimp. You've given pimps too much credit but I think you're a person with a serious problem. You need help because you've tried to play the game and you've not succeeded and now you're hurt and trying to take it out on vulnerable, unsuspecting women. You need to slow your roll because one of these days, you're going to run into the wrong woman and she's going to give you a taste of your own medicine!"

Douglas: I've already gotten an early taste of the medicine!"

Amos: "It sounds like you're in a vicious cycle of tit for tat."

Douglas: "No, it is tits and tapping and that's what I'm going to get ready to do. I'll talk to you later! I'm on my way to the pool—care to join me?"

Amos responds, "I don't know—I might come out there. I'm chillin' in the room for a minute. Maybe later." He pauses. "Okay, well, I'm getting a head start and I'll see you down there."

Scene: Julya is in her bathroom washing the makeup off her face and singing. She's talking aloud while she is washing the makeup off. Her phone rings and it is Pastor Danig.

Danig's voice can be heard on the phone. "How are you? I was just checking to see how things are going with you and your time away from you children."

Julya smiles and responds, "Things are good. I just spoke with them and my mom says they're asleep. They're pretty good," she contends. "I don't usually have too many problems with them. I try to keep them sheltered from all of the drama that's in my life."

Pastor Danig speaks with a pastoral-sounding voice, "Well, I was just checking and wanted to thank you again for a job well done. I've ran into a bit of controversy with my presentation but not everyone is against me on this one!"

Julya responds while smiling, "I figured something was going on because I observed some of the pastors' reactions while you were preaching and they didn't seem too accepting of some of the things you spoke about."

Pastor Danig, "You're absolutely right and I'm glad you mentioned this because I mentioned this in our meeting and the minister I spoke of tried to deny it. I can understand his response because my presentation was in contrast to what he spoke about on the previous night. I won't labor with our problems but I was just checking in with how things are going and if you need anything, just give me a call."

Julya's smile fades a bit and responds, "Okay, thanks, Pastor, and I'll do that."

Scene: Pastor Danig in hotel room talking to his wife:

Pastor Danig: "Honey, you know, the meeting was really tense. The ministers on staff from the various churches had major issues with what I presented. Only two ministers supported what I spoke about. Actually, it was one minister who spoke on my behalf when they all attacked me at the meeting. It was really sad because the other minister jumped on the bandwagon to support what I was saying simply when the other pastor indicated that more money was raised following my presentation. The interesting thing about all of that was that I did not hold any special offering nor did I set up a money line for people to give. I think it was pretty phony of the other pastor to try to act like he was supporting what I was talking about simply over the notion that more money was raised."

Maylee: "I'm sorry to hear that you weren't getting any support for the majority but as long as what you're doing is out of the word of God and God is pleased, I don't think you should worry about what they think."

Pastor Danig: "Well, honey, I have to be concerned because we are supposed to be on one accord on matters of the word. We cannot seem divided to the people that we're teaching and I saw a lot that going on. I tried to be mature on the matter but some of the ministers showed out in a big way."

"Well, honey, what do you expect? If you take a stand on something that you believe and it's in God's word, then of course, you're going to get opposition. The people you're working with will not always agree with you. Maybe you should do what they ask you and stop being such a rebel on everything. In fact, you should do what they ask, preach and speak the way the want you to because it seems as though you're listening to everything else that they're requesting of you."

Pastor Danig: "What are you saying?"

Maylee: "I think you know what I'm saying!"

Pastor Danig firmly responds, "Why don't you just be frank about what you're saying and stop mincing words, honey!"

Maylee responds, "Okay, I will give you an example. If they asked you to come on the trip without your spouse, why didn't you stand up to them and tell them that pastors need to be on trips like this with their wives? This is how you strengthen marriages by involving the spouse in all aspects of your life not separating them from it because you feel it is against business protocol. I think it is asinine to sit there and fight on the notion of giving and not address an important issue like wives accompanying their spouses on conference trips."

Danig: "Honey, you're trying to tell me when to take a stand on something. I didn't feel it was necessary to make an issue of the wives accompanying their husbands on a business trip. I was simply following a business procedure that fits the business model."

Maylee: "Fits the business model? Doesn't the church and the Bible support marriage? You're trying to get away from that by focusing on some business model. The church is behaving too much like a business and I see that you guys are mixing business with pleasure and while doing so, you're not even considering you spouses. It makes no sense for you to go to a hotel environment and not bring your spouse."

Pastor Danig: "Oh, so now what you're saying is that you don't trust me."

Maylee: "No, I think it is an appearance of evil and you are setting yourself up for some temptation that you might not be strong enough to get out of."

"Okay, hun, since I've been on this trip, I've been consecrating and studying the word and I don't think I should have to shun myself from opportunities to speak to people simply because you have a problem with the way it is done. I have to make judgment on things and I already told you that I needed to see what the environment was like before I just brought my wife along. Yes, I'm looking at this as a business trip and wives don't usually accompany their husbands on business trips. As I'm learning about these conferences, I'll use my discretion as to whether I should bring you."

Maylee: "So based on what you've seen thus far, will I be able to attend the next conference with you?"

Pastor Danig: "I don't see how, I've been busy the whole time and I don't think you would enjoy me in my focused world."

Maylee: "You have time to talk to me on the phone about your problems and you're obviously looking for some type of support because you're talking to me now. What's the difference? If I was there, you wouldn't have to be calling me! In fact, you could come to the hotel room and we could talk about it and even debrief in our own little way. I could have been in the audience and observed some things that you probably would not have seen because you'd be so focused on what you're teaching about. I could give you that perspective and help you. Isn't that what wives are supposed to do?"

Pastor Danig: "Yeah, and you can help by supporting me when I say that it is not a good idea that you attend a conference with me. Now, in response what you just said, I don't see how you being there would help the situation. Sitting in the audience might have caused them to act differently knowing that you were in the audience and able to observe reactions and responses. Okay, we can go around in circles on this but I choose to not do this. Anyway, hun, I must go, I have a call coming in. I'll call you back."

Maylee: "As usual, everything else is more important."

"I'll call you back and I'm going to address that last comment."

Pastor Danig clicks over and he knows it's Julya. He answers, "Hey, Julya, how's it going?"

Julya: "Well, Pastor, I was wondering if I could talk to you about something personal but I don't know if it is appropriate to do on the phone. Can we schedule a meeting to talk when the conference is over?"

Pastor Danig, "Well, Julya, we can do that or we could set something up right now if it cannot wait."

Julya: "Well, I thought I could wait because I know you're married and if anyone saw us together talking about anything, they would think something was going on. So I can wait."

"Well, if you must get it off your mind and need to speak sooner, I can arrange for it to not look like we're doing something outside of a counseling session."

Julya: "I don't feel comfortable, I'll just wait."

Pastor Danig: "If you feel otherwise just let me know."

Julya: "Okay, thank you. Goodbye!"

Pastor Danig: "Goodbye!" Pastor Danig returns the call to his wife. "So where were we?"

Maylee: "We were at the interruption of our phone conversation. Who was more important that required you to click over rather than just call back at a later time? I don't get the attitude. Why are you trying to tell me how to behave and what to say and do?"

Pastor Danig: "You are being controlling and I don't like it. You must have forgotten about the vows we took when we got married and you're behaving as though they mean nothing. I don't want to talk about anything right now because you are twisting everything I'm doing and trying to make me look as if I don't know what I'm doing."

Scene at poolside:

The musicians are sitting on the chairs with shades on looking at the interesting sights around the pool. Douglas gets into a booty rating game with the guitarist.

Douglas: "Every booty that comes by, you must rate it from 1-10 and give a reason for your rating."

One woman passes by in her 50s and the rating begins. They both tally up their scores and give their assessments.

"Okay, how would you rate those butt cheeks?"

Guitarist: "Well, I would give those an 8! Those butt cheeks are holding on with minimal sag from 50 years of gravitational pull, so I would give it a 5," said Douglas.

"Okay, here's the next candidate. A lady about 30ish is walking with a friend who's also in her late 20s, okay. We have to rate them both."

Douglas, "Okay, the one on the right is about a 9.98 and the one on the left is a 7."

Guitarist: "Okay, now why, Douglas?"

Douglas: "Okay, the 9.98 buttock is moving in a manner that indicates a level of sophistication and it is sitting firmly in the bikini without stressing the fabric. The one on the left, well, let's say that it gets a 7 because no woman should have an ass that moving in a different direction from where the person is walking. What is going on here, okay, now what's your rating, Mr. Guitarist?"

Guitarist: "Well, it seems that we have a difference of opinion. Well, I would give the one on the right a 5 and the one on the right a 10! The right has a buttock that is capable of holding a stack of books if necessary. It is too high and it doesn't sit correctly about her pelvic region. The one of the left deserves a 10 because the fullness of the butt matches the woman's body type. She's short and thick and the butt cheeks are large enough to allow for proper sitting in places where it's needed."

Douglas: "Okay, Mr. Guitarist, I hope you're keeping this rated G because our general audience would like to know the importance of being able to sit without reading into that last statement."

"Okay, let's do this last contestant that's approaching us at three o'clock. She's in her 30s and a bit on the slender side."

"Okay, I'm giving this one a 10," said Douglas, "for the reason that her butt is consistently round and tapers off to her legs oh so perfectly!"

The Guitarist: "Okay, again, we're in disagreement. I must tell you she's getting a 7 on this one! The butt is simply too large for her body type!"

Douglas changes his voice to sound like a commentator: "Bob, I gotta tell ya, she's not walking correctly and the butt cheeks are looking for a 'bebop'-style walk! Okay, so this concludes our program on the buttocks. Stay tuned for more buttock reviews when we return—same time and channel. See you soon!"

They both begin laughing when they notice one of the ministers getting into the Jacuzzi. He has boxers on and some shades and he's looking like a player.

The Guitarist: "Hey, man, you know that looks pretty nasty, this old man trying to be hip with the shades, the boxers and a sagging stomach. Who's he fooling and who does he expect to get?"

Douglas: "Well, I don't know, I thought he was married, so he shouldn't be trying to get anybody!"

"That's true, but I'm telling you these pastors are out here doing something and they're trying to be secretive with it. You know you cannot fool a player. You know when someone is up to something. They try to act cool and they put the shades on so they can look around undetected but they're on the prowl and they think no one knows about it. I'm on to their games and I think it's pretty deceptive. I know these ministers have their little secret stuff going on and they've managed to get away with it with the exception of a few who get caught when someone gets mad and decides to tell some media form or somebody. Yeah, we've heard the stories about these pastors messing around with young girls or boys for that matter. You hear this crazy stuff like some of these priests stopping themselves from being with a woman whom I think is unnatural and then they start looking at the altar boys. I see it almost like inmates who are shunned from the outside world and the closest thing to a woman is the other man in the cell."

Guitarist: "Interesting. Well, to be honest with you, I don't think I'll ever have a desire for another man. Don't be surprised, though, Douglas, if one of these ministers tries to come on to you because I heard that one of the ministers is on the down-low!"

Douglas: "You don't have to worry about me yielding to that mess, man, I like the ladies too much man."

Guitarist: "Okay, well, anyway, check out dude in the hot tub. He's checking out the ladies. Look how his head is slightly angling in the opposite direction as to where those two chicks are walking. That's the oldest trick in the book! Now watch how he moves his head to adjust to the move further away from his blind spot. He's looking! Do you see how his head is following those chicks? They know he's looking, too. Look at how they're walking. He's a bit unashamed at what he's doing because I know there's trouble in their paradise. Now, I must tell you that I know those other ministers are doing something. They're just real secretive about it and they may not come out here and do their corrupt stuff but do you notice that they disappear from this scene? They aren't having meetings anymore and they certainly aren't hanging with their wives because the wives are at home."

He laughs and Douglas says, "Well, maybe they're playing golf or something."

Guitarist: "Yeah, right! They're playing night golf with a glow-in-the-dark golf ball."

Douglas said, "Really, I didn't know they had that!"

They both laughed.

Guitarist: "Man, I don't care about what these player ministers are doing, I'm going to get in this pool and fraternize with some of these women."

Douglas: "Man, you go ahead, I'm just going chill out over here and watch you in action."

Scene at the hotel courtyard:

Pastor Danig receives another call from Julya.

"Can you arrange for us to sit and talk about the personal matter? I really don't want to wait and it probably won't take long."

Pastor Danig said, "Okay, you can meet me in the suite on the fourth floor. It's a meeting place for the staff and people are always there, so it won't look like we're going off somewhere alone."

Julya: "Well, that's sounds good but I hope no one will be able to hear what I'd like to talk to you about. Will this place allow for us to be able to talk without anyone hearing it?"

Pastor Danig: "Well, aside from speaking softly, someone is bound to hear something and you know how the walls have ears even when you think someone isn't listening, someone is listening."

Julya: "Well, I guess that leaves us to discussing it on the phone because I feel a lot better if no one would hear what I'm saying."

Pastor Danig: "Okay, I'm all ears!"

Julya: "I went to dinner with the drummer and he basically told me that he wanted to get to know me basically like a booty call. I feel I shouldn't be sharing this with you because I could have told him no but I thought it would have been an innocent gesture just going to dinner with a musician at the church."

Pastor Danig: "So how did it turn to a booty call, as you say?"

Julya: "Well, it was the conversation we had and he alluded to the fact that people aren't here solely for spiritual purposes. He basically said that people here are not here for church matters but they are getting their freaks on! Is this true?"

Pastor Danig: "Well, I don't know what people are doing at these conferences or outside of what we're doing but you cannot monitor what adults are doing. We are at a hotel, vacation environment and some of the single people in the ministry might use this as an opportunity to socialize a bit and hopefully it's with people they know. I'm not an advocate of socializing to the point of using people for sexual gratification but some people are playing games that are pretty deceptive and if you're not keen, you'll fall into that trap regardless of how knowledgeable you think you are."

Julya: "I get what you're saying but I think Douglas was saying that people at this conference are cheating and doing all sorts of wild sneaky stuff behind their significant other's backs. I cannot believe that this could be happening at a church event!"

Pastor Danig: "I don't know what you might have heard but if someone is doing something wrong, they're going to have to answer to God. If they are members of the church and are doing things against the Bible and it becomes known, then those individuals will need counseling."

Julya: "I think it's more than someone doing something wrong and having to answer to God but I'm saying that it's like significant people on the conference committee know that wrongdoing is going on and no one is addressing it or correcting the behavior. In fact, it is like it is being advocated rather than reproving the people that are behaving this way. What's that all about?"

Danig: "I'm new to the conference and I pretty much consumed in my own affairs to really consider the social activities that might or might not be going on."

Julya: "So you're saying that there are some strange things that might be going on?"

Danig: "I don't involve myself in rumors nor do I choose to spend too much time on these matters."

Julya: "Well, I decided to get a little social on this conference and accepted an invitation to dinner with Douglas and I feel it didn't go well. I think the attitude was all wrong and when he didn't like what I was saying he rejected me in a roundabout way, which was cool because I didn't like him either."

Pastor Danig: "Well, I think it was courteous of you to give him the opportunity to spend time with a beautiful and grounded lady."

Julya: "Now I'm going to ask you a question and this a hypothetical one so don't take it seriously. You have to promise me that you will answer honestly and without politicizing and sounding like a pastor. Just give me your honest response. Now how would you respond if I asked you to dinner and I told you it was strictly platonic?"

Pastor Danig: "Huh, well, I wouldn't go with you simply because I'm a married man and it appears evil."

Julya: "You said it appears evil but it isn't evil. So if something appears evil, does it mean that it's evil?"

Pastor Danig: "Not all of the time. There could be something good or innocent behind what appears to be evil."

Julya: "So going to dinner with you isn't evil if my intention is to have dinner and discuss business. I think it becomes evil if there is a motive behind it. That is, if I'm trying to stage an opportunity for you to get to know me and perhaps get you to like me. But if my intentions are pure and you're weak, then I would have innocently set the stage for something evil to take place."

Pastor Danig: "Well, perhaps that's where shunning the appearance of evil comes into play because both parties might be innocent and the end results might be evil."

Julya: "How is that evil if the people coming together might be destined to be together?"

Pastor Danig: "Well, that isn't the case here as I'm married."

Julya: "I wasn't referring to you or us for that matter, Pastor."

Pastor Danig: "Okay, well, I think if we went to dinner with innocent intentions and having information about two individuals of the opposite sex who are attractive or with personalities that are suitable, there's a possibility that it might go further than what was intended."

Julya: "Sounds reasonable. Okay, so me going to dinner with Douglas was an appearance of evil."

Pastor Danig: "Well, I don't see how if you're single and he's single. But, it might look evil if the people observing know something about the individuals. For that matter forget about people making the observation. What do you know about the situation?"

Julya: "Well, going to dinner might help to find out about the situation. So the appearance of evil occurs when one is gathering information."

Danig: "You know they slandered Jesus' name when he was in places healing and getting people delivered. These weren't the type of places where you'd find men of God hanging around but he was on a mission."

Julya: "What do you mean?"

"Well, suppose there was a friend or someone who had information about one of the individuals and knew that they were out to dinner with a different woman every night. That would be an appearance of evil because that person is classified as a player and you, the victim, are being played in the sight of others."

Julya: "So you're saying Douglas is a player—I figured that!"

Danig: "I didn't say that but I gathered you must have found out some-thing that was displeasing as you said it didn't go well."

Julya: "Well, if we were able to go to dinner at a place where no one would be able to view it as an appearance of evil, then is it an appearance of evil that we should shun if the intentions aren't evil?"

Pastor Danig: "Well, going to a place where no one would view it as evil is equivalent to sneaking. That in itself has an appearance of evil."

Julya: "You're being logical."

Pastor Danig laughs: "I hope my logic has a connection with the word."

Julya: "I just wanted to address my concerns with you because prior to coming to this trip, I was told to be on the lookout for players who are in high positions. My mom shared some things that she experienced in some ministry she was involved in some years ago."

Pastor Danig: "Ministries have these challenges and I think the problems we experience here can happen everywhere. It isn't something confined to one ministry but where people interact in any setting, there's the probability for some problems. The sad notion is that when something goes wrong in a church environment, it stands out because of the perception of how church people should behave. People expect church dynamics to be perfect and it won't because imperfect people are working in ministry."

Julya: "But I think church people should behave at a higher standard knowing that people look up to them."

Pastor Danig: "If they are reading the scriptures and given the proper guidance by their leaders then these problems would be minimal. Well, I'm going to use the school teacher example. When you hear of a school teacher doing something inappropriate with a student, it makes the news. Now, no teacher should interact in any sexual way with a student but there are those who act on their behaviors and risk their careers and adversely impact the life of some young, inexperienced youth who doesn't know any better. Maybe the analogy with an airplane that crashes. You do realize that airline travel is the safest way to travel. In fact, people who are afraid to fly don't realize that it is actually safer than driving but because we look at the tragedy involved when a plane does crash, that seems to be the thing that stays seated in our minds. When we look at the church and hear of something like a pastor being involved with a secretary when he is married or perhaps a homosexual relationship when you know many of them preach against it, it stands out. People withdraw from the church and anything linked to church because anything negative will stand out more than good even if the good outweighs the negative. So I find myself working with people who try to justify their behaviors by using the weakness of the flesh as an excuse to partake in lascivious and other activities that they know are wrong. They want to use this notion that Jesus died on a cross for their sins as their saving grace to get to heaven. I think some have the mentality that 'let me see how much wrong I can do and still get to heaven. After all, Jesus died on the cross for my iniquities and I should still get in right because I believe.' But then there are scriptures that God expects us to live a righteous life. Shall we continue in sin that grace may abound. Jesus told sinners whom he healed to go and sin no more. We have to realize that when you know something, that's where the higher standard comes in. We need to be rebuked when it comes to knowing something and then pretending that we don't know. God knows our heart and we're only fooling ourselves. The scripture lets us know that if we know something and decide to go in the opposite direction, God is going to hold us accountable in a greater way."

Julya: "So you're saying that if we know that we're sinning and we don't take action to put a stop to it, we are going to be punished in a greater way?"

Danig: "I think that there is a consequence for sin. If you know something is wrong and you do it, then you're taking the side of the sin. Our fleshly nature wants to do wrong and I really don't know why but that's the way we were created."

Julya: "I'm confused. It seems that God created us with issues and then he had a plan to save us from ourselves by having Jesus die for our sins. Why would God create us with these issues and then save us from ourselves or from an eternal suffering because of our nature?"

Danig: "I think we know in part about God's plan for us and if we study the word every day, some things will make sense while other things won't. That's where the faith comes in."

Julya: "That seems ridiculous and almost like the easy answer out to a difficult question."

Pastor Danig: "You might not understand everything and we can have think-tank discussions about the 'whys' in everything but if we trust in God, some of those answers to those questions might make sense while others won't. There is a mystery to Godliness and God in his omniscience has us knowing in part. Man wanted to be like God and he let the devil fool him into have knowledge and being like God. I think from that point on, it was the flaw in flesh to be like God and that isn't possible because God is a Holy Spirit and there are limitations in the flesh."

Julya: "I'm still confused and want to know more. Can we sit down and discuss this more? I really want to know and grow in God's word. I think this is incredible that the Bible is a holy book that we can read and search the scriptures to get closer to God and find out what God's plan is in our lives. I've been through enough mess in my life that I desire wanting to get some answers."

Pastor Danig: "I'm so glad to hear you speak this way. I'm looking forward to seeing you at our Bible classes and if you are really interested in taking your studying of the word to the next level, I can recommend one of the local Bible colleges. You do know that our staff gets tuition reimbursement for attending colleges in our network. That would be great for you as you don't have to worry about extra expenditures when you're trying to raise your children as a single mom."

Julya: "Well, thank you for that information. Okay, I'm going to get off this phone, my teeth are bothering me. Do you know if the gift shop sells Ambesol because I need relief now?"

Pastor Danig: "I think they do and while it's on my mind, you do realize that your insurance includes a dental plan. Did you enroll in one of the dental plans that we have?"

Julya: "Yes, I did, but I've been so busy with work, school and raising these kids that every time I set up an appointment, I'm cancelling it because something always comes up."

Pastor Danig: "Well, I don't mean to sound like I'm preaching to you on this one but make sure you find time for yourself, that is take care of your health. Your teeth have to be healthy because infections in your mouth can affect other parts of your body. So as your pastor and knowing that your body is the temple—make an appointment and stick to it. Tell everyone it's an emergency and that you must get this done!"

Scene: Dentist's office:

Julya is sitting in the waiting room and awaiting her name to be called. She begins reading one of the magazines on the table. The flat-screen TV is playing in the background and the high0frequency sound of drills can be heard in the background. A dental assistant comes out to the waiting room and calls Julya and she places the magazine on the table and grabs her purse. She squeezes past a teenager girl with braces and thick glasses and who is chewing gum.

The dental assistant says, "We're going to take you in this room to get X-rays and then in about 15 minutes, we'll let you know what needs to be done. The dentist will speak to you and explain the procedure and options."

Julya: "Thank you."

Julya sits in a semi-supine position in the chair and the technician tells her, "I'm going to be taking a few pictures and I'm going to place something in your mouth in order to take these pictures."

Julya: "I thought you were doing X-rays?"

Tech: "You're absolutely right. We are taking pictures using the X-ray machine."

Julya: "Okay, well, how safe is this?"

"It's pretty safe as the level of X-radiation is low. We cover you with this lead blanket to protect your reproductive organs."

Julya: "Why do you need to protect my reproductive organs if the X-ray is shooting rays in my mouth? Isn't that close to my brain? Shouldn't I have a lead hat around my head or something?"

Tech: "No worry, the lead blanket is an extra precautionary measure because the cells of your reproductive system are actively dividing and might be more sensitive to any exposure to X-rays. We do it as a precaution because—the minimal rays don't actually come near those areas anyway."

Julya: "Okay, I ask lots of questions!"

Tech: "No problem. It's good to know something about the treatments you're getting."

Julya, thinking to herself: "I'm going to get all of the questions out now because I realize that I won't be doing much talking when they numb my mouth with the anesthesia."

The tech places the plastic-like bendable structures in Julya's mouth and asks her to bite down. Julya makes a face as the plastic structures are uncomfortable when she bites down. The tech removes the structure and places another between the gums and her tongue and asks her to bite down again.

Julya gets frustrated and asks, "How many more of these do we have to do?"

The tech asks Julya to bite down and then angles the arm-like structure of the X-ray machine toward her mouth. She then says, "Hold still while I take the picture." She leaves the room, takes the picture and returns. She does this eight times. On the last one the tech says, "Okay, this is the last one," and Julya's response is a sigh of relief.

Julya: "Thank God, because this is more aggravating that the actual dental work. Those plastic things are uncomfortable and it's digging all down in my soft tissue between my gums. All this technology and you guys don't have a better way to take pictures in somebody's mouth!"

Tech: "Hopefully one day they'll have a much easier more comfortable way to do this. I agree with you, it can be a bit uncomfortable." The tech finishes the job and escorts Julya to another room. Tech: "Okay, the dentist will be in here in a few minutes to talk to you about what needs to be done."

Julya: "Okay."

Ten minutes later, the dentist arrives and says, "How are you? I'm Dr. Stein and I'd like to talk to you about your teeth. Well, you have a cavity and it's infected. We need to clean out the cavity and see if we save the tooth."

Julya: "Save the tooth?"

Dr. Stein: "Yes, your tooth is badly infected all the way down into the root. We can do a root canal or simply remove the tooth. Your insurance pays for most of the work for the root canal and if you choose to have the tooth removed, you won't have to pay anything."

Julya: "I'm nervous about root canals and I certainly don't want a space in my mouth. Those are the only options that I have?"

"Well, the root canal is good option and it isn't as bad as you're probably imagining."

Julya: "The thought of you drilling through my teeth and pulling nerves out of my teeth gives me the creeps. I mean, why do you have to take the nerves out? Can you just take treat the infection?"

"Well, it will be difficult to treat the infected canal without removing the nerves."

Julya: "Don't I need my nerves?"

Dr. Stein: "Well, the nerves in your teeth help your teeth feel or sense hot or cold."

Julya: "I don't think I want to be without that sensation. Wouldn't that tooth feel numb? I don't know if I want one of my teeth to have a numb feeling."

Dr. Stein: "Well, it will probably feel a lot better than the pain you're experiencing from an infected tooth. This infected tooth will infect other areas of your body and cause other health problems. If you choose the other option of having your tooth removed, then you will have to consider the problem of your teeth spacing out or moving over the years because there is no tooth sitting in that section of bone. The other teeth will tend to shift. Now removing the tooth still gives you the option of having bridge work or an implant so that that section of bone continues to have the needed pressure as is the case with the other teeth imbedded in the bone."

Julya: "I'm ready for relief from this pain, so let's go with the root canal."

Dr. Stein: "Okay, I'm going to have to inject you with anesthesia so that you won't feel discomfort from all of the drilling and cleaning."

Julya observes. He grabs a swab and dips it in a brown jelly-like substance. He takes this and rubs it on the gums and places gauze in her mouth. She could feel the tingling sensation as the dentist begins preparing the syringe. Her palms started sweating and she could feel her heart racing. Julya thought to herself, "It is a rather long needle and I'm wondering if he's going to inject this all the way into my gums."

Dr. Stein: "Okay, Julya, you're just going to feel a little pinch."

He starts pushing the needled into the soft flesh of her gums and pushes further until the entire needle has penetrated. He slowly pushes the syringe and empties the contents of the anesthesia deep into Julya's gums. He slowly withdraws the syringe and then gets another syringe.

Julya: "You're going to do this again?"

Dr. Stein: "You need another injection and then we're going to wait about ten minutes. You know the anesthesia will begin to make your jaw and lower mouth feel numb."

As he was talking he quickly injected the other needle in the mouth and then before you knew it, he removed it. She was relieved that she survived the long needle and now the next bout with the drilling. The high-frequency sounds of those drills make her feel that something insane is happening to people. Why are these drills being used in someone's mouth?

She could hear drills in the background going on in the other rooms. As she waited, the numbing accompanied with tingling increased and then the doctor walks in the door.

"Okay, how does your mouth feel?"

Julya answered like her mouth was being filled with food. "It's numb."

Dr. Stein: "Well, that's good."

The dental assistant walks in and then begins arranging things on the table to her right. The doctor adjusts the light and begins looking with the hand mirror. The assistant gives him a plastic piece to help me keep the mouth open.

Dr. Stein: "Okay, I'm going to begin cleaning out the tooth with this drill and raise your hand if you feel any discomfort."

Julya thought to herself, "Why would I feel discomfort through all of this anesthesia and numbness?"

The dentist starts the dreaded drill and begins drilling the tooth. Julya could feel the pressure but the numbing from the anesthesia that made her toothache problem disappear made the drilling tolerable. It seemed as though he was using some technique to get through the tooth enamel as he pressed the drill for a second and pulled back. The times when he held the drill against the tooth for a longer period caused her to feel a surging electrical-like feeling through her jaw.

Julya immediately raised her hand and mumbled, "Feeling discomfort."

She nodded her head and then he said, "Okay," waited for a moment and then began drilling again.

He continued drilling while the assistant was controlling the suctioning device. Some debris became airborne and was easily visible as it reflected off the light. The sound of the suctioning device and the drill made it seem as though a major event at a construction site was underway. The sound of the drill sped up and slowed down as it encountered more tooth enamel. He finally stopped drilling for a moment and then took out a tool and stuck it in the drilled-out tooth. He removed something and then when it was all done, he said, "Okay, we successfully removed the nerves from your tooth. Now we will clean and disinfect the tooth."

Julya's thoughts: "It was music to my ears hearing that they were nearly done and I felt like it was a workout for me. I felt tired even though I sat in a chair and they were doing all of the work!"

He finally finished and said, "Your other teeth look fine and we'll just do a deep cleaning and be done for today."

Scene: Pastor Danig's home:

Pastor Danig finally makes it home from the conference and greets his wife at the door. She is happy to see him and greets him with a tight hug and a kiss.

Maylee: "So how was your trip, honey?"

Pastor Danig: "It was interesting. I have a lot to talk about but for now, I'd like to unwind with a bath in my own bathtub and get some of what I smell in the kitchen. Oh, it smells so good, honey."

Maylee: "I'll get it ready for you, hun."

Pastor Danig: "Well, I'm going to do the bath thing first, I just need thirty minutes."

Pastor Danig enters the room and Maylee is in the kitchen getting dinner ready. She looks over at the counter and notices the phone as it lights up. It is Julya calling. Maylee wonders who could possibly be calling moments after her husband has returned from a long trip. The number is restricted but Maylee decides to ignore any negative thoughts for the time being. She continues working on getting the food ready when the phone makes a message signal.

Maylee: "That must have been a long message—why did it take so long for the phone to signal?"

After about 25 minutes, Maylee says, "Dinner is about ready, hun."

Danig: "Okay, I'll be out in a minute."

Scene at Julya's home:

Julya, on phone with baby's daddy: "When are you going to pay some child support? I just got back from a business trip and I need some funds."

Baby's Daddy: "Business trip? Bitch, you going on business trips and asking me for money—I should be asking you for money! You know my situation and when I get some damn money, you'll get some!"

Julya: "See, that's the problem! You have no respect and you shouldn't be calling me crazy names like that because I'm still the mother of your children!"

Baby's Daddy: "You need to shut the fuck up because you never had a problem with me saying 'bitch' when we were having sex!"

Julya: "You don't need to go there because we were both cussing and we're not doing that anymore!"

Baby's Daddy: "Well, whenever you want something from me you'll end up coming around and letting me give you what you like."

Julya: "Don't flatter yourself, fool! As a matter of fact, I've grown past your immaturity and gangsta ways!"

Baby's Daddy: "What?"

Julya: "Yes, and I want you to think about when your mom said how excited and crazy you were over those Tonka trucks you used to play with. Do you still have the same excitement about those toys and do you still play with your Tonkas?"

Baby's Daddy: "Bitch, are you fuckin' crazy? I'm not playing with no damn Tonkas! Those toys are the furthest thing from my mind outside of having to buy them for our kids!"

Julya: "Good, I'm glad you understand how I feel about you and if you call me a bitch again!"

Baby's Daddy interrupts: "Yeah, now you think you're all uppity and shit with your illustrations and shit. You've been hanging around preachers that love using illustrations and telling little stories to wheel you in before they take your money! Ain't none of them preachers different them me! I'm out here hustling for the dollar and they're doing the same thing! The only difference is that I admit that my shit is foul but they coat theirs with cologne and hope that no one can smell the shit! Let me give you an illustration You ever tried putting perfume on and you didn't wash that ass? I can still smell the shit! And just to let you know, there ain't nothing real about these fake preachers! You want to play the stupid game because they look good on the surface, just like I did!"

Julya: "Not every minister is a hypocrite and you might learn something from the ones who are doing the right thing!"

Baby's Daddy: "Don't talk to me about what I can learn from some scheming preacher! You must be crazy to think that I'd listen to some phony preacher who's living lavishly off the money of others!" The baby's daddy contorts his face and yells, "Otha mutha-fuckin' people's money! OMPMs!" He starts laughing and then says, "Didn't you learn that in college? You didn't think I knew about that, huh." Yeah, that's the problem with you college-educated wanna-beeesss. My street smarts let me make the kinda money and as corrupt as you think it is, I'm doing business with people who consent to the stuff that you think is corrupt. You, on the other hand, are working with fraudulent mothafuckas who act like they working for the Lord and taking your money and womanizing and manizing every corrupt thing you can think of. You're naïve because you on some little payroll and you think they're helping you out. Like I said, it is a matter of time before one of the phony preachers makes an inappropriate move on you! It's probably going on right now but you're too stupid to see it. Now let me ask you this! Are any preachers at your church being extra nice to you?"

Julya: "They're behaving like people do in the work environment."

Baby's Daddy: "You will soon find out that I'm right and then you're gonna come running to me because what I got for you is the real thing. I ain't hiding behind the Bible or using the Bible for corruption. I'm as real as they come!"

Julya: "Yeah, you're a genuine thug that needs deliverance and hopefully before it's too late. Are you going to pay some money to support your children? Just drop it off as soon as you can! I gotta go!"

Baby's Daddy: "Yeah, run off to your sanctified hypocrites!"

Scene: Pastor Danig enters the kitchen and hugs his wife from behind as she's serving his plate.

Pastor Danig: "Wow, that smells good. I don't care how fancy the restaurant is! There is nothing like homecooked food!"

Maylee: "Well, there's nothing like having a wife that's home and waiting on her husband."

Pastor Danig: "What is that supposed to mean?"

Maylee: "Well, you have to understand my position. I'm home with the kids while you're out doing church business and sometimes it seems like you don't understand. I think if the shoe was on the other foot, you wouldn't be quiet about this."

Pastor Danig: "So you're saying if you were a pastor and had to travel I would have a problem with it."

Maylee: "You would absolutely have a problem with it. I don't understand why women have to put up with the patriotic, macho mess because a man wants to use an excuse that he's bringing home the bacon. I don't even like pork so I don't even know what people are always talking about bacon! I don't understand women who feel they need to shut up and put up with a lifestyle that is uncomfortable to the psyche simply because of a paycheck. You would not like the fact that I would go away for three days at a time with the scandalous stuff that's going on."

Pastor Danig: "Well, you're a woman and it would be dangerous for you to travel alone."

Maylee: "This is what I'm talking about! See, I can hire a bodyguard and go on a trip for a few days and you would have a problem with it. It wouldn't matter if it was business related."

Danig: "I wouldn't have a problem with it if you were bringing home the bacon. I would let you do your thing because I trust you."

Maylee: "You know you're full of it. You have a problem if I'm away for a few hours kicking with my girlfriends.

Danig: "Are you serious? Do you honestly think that?"

Maylee: "Always blowin' up my phone when you're home with the children and I'm just trying to get a couple of hours. Just imagine more than a day. You'd be on the next flight to where I'm conducting my business. But you had a problem with me coming along and being your helpmate. Now I know some of those pastors must have brought their wives and if none of them brought their wives, then it sounds a bit suspicious. Why would men of God not want to bring their wives?"

Pastor Danig: "Now I'm not going to go down that road with you again. We already went over that and I'm tired and don't want to bicker after a long trip. Can I sit down and enjoy some of this homecooked food?"

Maylee: "Again, you're evading the issue and I just don't understand why you can't answer my questions."

Danig: "I'll answer your questions as soon as I get some of this good food in my system. Deal? I will answer all of the questions you have after I get something to eat."

Maylee walks into the other room and makes a phone call. She's talking to her mom about visiting in the summer. Maylee: "I'm thinking about visiting in the summer. My husband won't be coming because he's really busy and I think this will be a good opportunity for me to go somewhere without him because that is what I'm dealing with on a regular basis."

Maylee's mom: "Okay, so what's wrong, sweetie? Your husband is a man of the cloth and I'm sure he's out doing God's work! You have to give him a break because he is doing what's right for you and your family. You are blessed to have a man that loves God and who is trying to be a good husband."

Maylee: "Mom, you don't understand! You're obviously on the outside and you're looking in on a problem that you don't fully understand!"

Maylee's mom: "Well, I don't have to fully understand what you're probably going through but I must say that you're not going to solve any problem that you have by trying to seek vengeance."

Maylee: "I'm not seeking vengeance."

Maylee's mom: "Well, you just said that you're coming to visit without your husband and that he does this to you when he goes on business trips."

Maylee: "Well, he does and I'm not seeking vengeance. He needs to know what it feels like when I go somewhere without him. I don't get it, Mom, it seems like everyone is on the side of the pastor. Everyone wants to look at the man of God as perfect and always doing the right thing. What about the wife of the man of God? Does anyone really understand what we have to go through?"

Maylee's mom. "Well, you need to count your blessings, sweetie. You should be grateful that the man you're married to isn't some pimp or drug dealer. You should be grateful that he loves you and the children and that he isn't out there running around living a double lifestyle, like some people. If he's in the word, then he will do right by you and I think he's one of those sincere ministers."

Maylee: "You don't understand! I don't think anyone should just sit back and act like we should just be grateful when there's a problem that must be addressed. I don't get it. So we should just sit back and let things happen without expressing how these events make us feel. I wouldn't be with a pimp or a drug dealer. Some people might sit back and live that type of lifestyle perhaps because they feel they don't have a choice. I don't think I'm just going to hang around, allow my husband to be away all the time, and then years go by and most of his time has been away doing ministry stuff. I know there are people on the staff that can help out and he doesn't have to be at every event nor does he have to go conferences without his wife."

Maylee's mom: "Sweetie, did you talk to him about your concerns?"

Maylee: "Yeah, Mom, and he just let me know that he's at work and that he needed to see what the conference atmosphere was like before bringing family along."

Maylee's mom: "Well, at least he let you know that he needs to see what it's like. You need to give him a chance to work in ministry. Support him and don't complain too much because that will push him away. In fact, if the ministers are allowed to bring their spouses, you want to let him know that if he brought you along, that it would be a wonderful trip and not one where you guys would be fussing over silly stuff. He certainly doesn't need to be around his colleagues in the ministry all stressed out or bickering with his spouse. People can tell when there's trouble in paradise. You cannot hide it—even with the phony and fake smiles—people can see right through that."

Scene: Pastor is in bedroom with his wife. They are both lying in bed; he is reading a book with glasses hanging slightly off his nose and she is crocheting a hat:

Maylee: Honey, I'm thinking about going home to visit family over the summer."

Pastor Danig: "That sounds great! How long are you planning on staying?"

Maylee: "My mom is having some problems with her arthritis and I'm going to spend about a couple of weeks down there to help out."

Pastor Danig: "Okay, that sounds good. So what month are you thinking of going down there?"

Maylee: "I'm thinking immediately after the kids get out of school. That's around the middle of June. That's what I'm doing now. I'm trying to find a really good flight through Travelocity." Maylee pauses and waits for a reaction.

Danig: "Hmmm, that's interesting. I have a friend at the church who works for the airlines who could get you some really good tickets but it will be standby."

Maylee: "Look, I don't have time for standby. Were you standing by when you went on your business trip?"

Pastor Danig: "No, I was just trying to save some money. Standby isn't so bad and—"

Maylee: "I'm taking the children and it isn't the same when you're trying to get somewhere and a standby flight might cause you to wait for the next flight if the one you're standing by is full. I'm not going to be inconvenienced like that to save a few dollars. I can't believe you would suggest such a thing when I'm taking the children."

Pastor Danig: "That's why I suggested it—because you're taking the children and we need to save some money."

Maylee: "Okay, so what, you're not the least bit concerned about your wife traveling with the children—enough to try to make it a bit more convenient for her? I don't understand you. You have even said that you would like to go on the trip with me. You just brushed it off and probably are looking forward to me going. You'll have some alone time to do your ministry, huh? Well? You should have suggested that the children stay with you. You know I'm going to help my mother and it will be hard to manage that with the children."

Pastor Danig: "Okay, leave the children with me—I'll manage them with the busy schedule that I have. You know that June is a big month for the ministry."

Maylee: "Yeah, it's a big month for the ministry. Well, you'll be able to manage, I'm sure. My sister can help you with the kids if you need it."

Pastor Danig: "I don't need help with the kids. You probably don't think I can manage the kids without you but I want you to know that I can do that and handle the work at the church."

Maylee: "For two weeks? I don't think you can do that without any help."

Scene at Julya's home:

Julya answers the door at her apartment and it's her baby's daddy. She opens the door partially and asks, "Why are you here so late, I'm tired and I just got back from the trip."

"Well, I just came by to give you something for the kids."

"Okay." Julya reaches out to grab the envelope and he pulls back and says, "Can I come in at least?"

"No, the kids are asleep and I'd like to go back to sleep."

Baby's Daddy: "Well, I'll just come back some other time."

He walks away and as he is walking, Julya says, "Don't come over here late in the evening trying to give me something because I don't know what you're really trying to give me!"

Baby's Daddy: "I tried giving you some money but you didn't want it so don't say anything!"

Scene: eight months later: Pastor Danig's wife is packing luggage in preparation for the trip to her family in Savanna, Georgia. She's on the phone with her sister while she is packing:

Maylee: "You know he's going to ask for your help while I'm gone. He's pretending that he can handle his workload and the children without my help. I can guarantee that he will be blowing up my phone and calling you to watch the children so he can do his ministry stuff. He's playing this little game because he's trying to prove a point about me going on a trip by myself without him asking to come along or without him calling me for help while I'm away."

Her sister laughs. "He probably won't call because he has his ego to protect."

Maylee: "I don't think his ego is stronger than the stresses that will force him to call for help. He will be so upset with the idea of having to work and come home and do the homemaking duties that so many people look at as menial. Did you know that if they included the homemakers in the Gross Domestic Product, it would be a trillion-dollar industry?"

Sister: "I didn't know that!"

Maylee: "Girl, it is so important and it is amazing how organized one must be to maintain a smooth running and clean household! You know as much as I do about planning the day and doing multiple tasks! You have to plan in advance so that the dinner is ready when the kids and the husband come home. You have to help the kids with homework and make sure they are doing their chores."

Sister: "I don't think he's going to call you. He will not let you know that he cannot do the house thing without your help. He's going to put up this front that he can handle it and when it is time for his next business trip, he's not going to have any reservations about telling you that he's going on his own and that you being with the children is an easy job."

Maylee: "Well, I don't think you're right on this one at all because I'm going to be gone for two weeks. He used to blow up my phone when I was gone for a day."

Sister: "The kids are older now and you guys just had an argument about his business trip. What better opportunity for him to prove you wrong. You just gave him the proving ground to prove you wrong."

Scene: Maylee is packing the suitcase for the trip to visit her parents:

Maylee is on the phone with her husband: "Honey, what time do you think you'll make it home because you know I have to be at the airport at least two hours early because of all the security checks?"

Pastor Danig: "Yes, I know, I know! Come on, honey, I travel enough to know this and don't worry, I won't have you late for your flight. In fact, your flight isn't until this evening and I'm leaving at noon."

Maylee: "Okay, are you sure you'll be able to handle both of the children?"

Pastor Danig: "I'll be able to handle it. I don't understand why you're worrying so much. These are my kids and I can handle my kids."

Wife: "I'm just going by why happened in the past. I don't want you stressing out and causing me to have to leave a little earlier than I plan."

Pastor Danig: "You're absolutely wrong on this one. That was a completely different situation. Our son was sick and you needed to be there."

Maylee: "Okay, I'm just trying to make sure because I don't want to come home and you're super frustrated because you didn't have time to do anything or you had problems on your job because you couldn't focus because something the kids were doing! I want you to know that this isn't a vacation for me. My mother is ill and I'm going there to help out a bit. I hope you understand that."

Pastor Danig: "It doesn't' matter whether you were going to relax or whether you were going in a work capacity, I can handle my children and none of that has any bearing on what happens while you're away."

Maylee: "Well, that's what you're saying now. Sometimes when we're stressed, in our minds we think something like this. 'Well, my Maylee is on vacation and I'm working and struggling to keep the household in order.' You might become frustrated because you're doing both tasks while it seems that I'm out having a good time."

Pastor Danig: "You just get ready to go on your trip and stop worrying about me. Well, I'll be home in a couple of hours and I'm sure you'll be ready to walk out the door when I get there. We can beat the rush-hour traffic if we leave as soon as I get there."

Maylee: "Okay, sweetie, I'll be ready when you get here."

"Goodbye...."

As soon as he hangs up, he walks over to the area where Julya is working on her computer. He passes her desk and says, "How are you this morning?"

"I'm fine," she replied. "Well, Pastor, can I share something with you?"

Pastor Danig: "What's that, Julya?"

"It's private and I don't want to discuss it out in the open, you know the walls have ears!"

Pastor Danig: "Well, give me five minutes and you can meet me in the office over there."

Julya: "Okay."

Pastor Danig walks over to the kitchen area and prepares a coffee. He then walks over to the refrigerator and pulls out a box of donuts and selects the chocolate-glazed flavor donut.

Scene: *Julya and the pastor are in the office room:*

Pastor Danig: "Okay, Julya, what did you have to talk about that required some privacy?"

Julya: "Well, I'm having problems on the home-front and I don't want it to impact my job."

Pastor Danig raises his eyebrow and says, "Well, it seems that you've been coming to work on time and your personal life doesn't seem to affect your professional one."

Julya: "Well, it isn't at this time but I'm a bit worried about my baby's daddy. He is a gangsta type and he visited me last night to give me child support money but he wanted something else in exchange, if you know what I mean. I don't like him like that and I don't want to sell out over child support money. That is his responsibility and I think he should mail it to me. I felt like I was in some sort of danger last night when he came over. He had that look in his eye like he wanted to do something but I immediately slammed the door after he walked off with the money since he didn't get what he wanted."

Pastor Danig: "The solution to your problem is to make an arrangement for him to mail it to you like you said or put him in the system and let them collect. If you don't want to have any dealings with him and feel that you're in danger, you might want to get a restraining order. Now, I don't know the details of your situation but I think you owe it to yourself and the children to make arrangements so that all of you feel safe and not have to worry about someone showing up at late hours of the night."

"Okay, Pastor, and thank you for the advice. I don't think I want to put him in the system because he warned me that I would not get anything if I did that. He's not working a regular job and it would be difficult for the system to get money from his wages if he didn't cooperate."

Pastor Danig: "Well, that isn't your problem. You need to do what is right for you and your children and you don't need someone who is potentially dangers to come around and put you or the kids in jeopardy. If he's living that gangsta lifestyle, there's no telling what he might do the next time he comes over. He might be filled with some type of drug and might force his way in your home. He might feel that since you guys have children together, that he has a right to come in there and do whatever he wants. You guys need to talk this over and if you can't come up with a resolution to this problem, then you'll have to go to the system. It's that simple. You'll end up in a vicious cycle with this guy and the money you're getting from him is probably money he's getting illegally."

Julya nods her head: "Well, I hope not. I don't want dirty money in my household."

Pastor Danig: "Well, I don't know if the money is dirty but if he's living a gangsta lifestyle, he's probably getting the money illegally."

Julya: "Well, I think he does odd jobs like construction on the side and he helps his uncle out at the auto shop."

"Okay, well, you are concerned about something, otherwise you would not have asked for this meeting. It's a good thing to take care of this now before it escalates into something more serious. Let me ask you this. Do you see you guys ever working things out and getting together in a serious relationship and then hopefully marriage? I don't put anything past God. I know he can deliver people even in situations that look like there's no way out."

Julya: "I don't like him enough to want to be with him in a serious relationship or marriage. Even if he changed, I would not want to be with him this way. He is immature and he's a womanizer and I don't think he'll ever change."

Scene: *Julya is on her way home from church and her baby's daddy is sitting in his car waiting for her:*

He notices her car leaving the church's parking lot and then he follows her. She stops by the grocery store and he parks in the same lot and waits for her. She goes into the grocery store and picks up a few items for him. As she returns to the car, he meets her in the parking lot and says, "Here's the money I tried to give you last night."

She pauses and says, "I don't like you coming over my place late in the evening like that. It is inappropriate!"

Baby's Daddy: "Inappropriate! You trying to sound smart or are you so stupid that you cannot see what's in front of you? I am the father of those children and I'm trying to give you support! It's really funny how you complain that you don't get enough money and when I'm ready to give it you complain about how I'm giving it to you. You don't seem to understand that when I get some money, I try to give it to you right away, because if I don't, I'm going to spend it on somebody else."

Julya: "And that's just it, it is inappropriate because you're bringing the money at such a late hour because some of them other bitches that you hang with aren't available. So you're trying to come over here and give me money with hopes that I'm going to give you something. I already told you that I'm not doing that anymore! I used to fall into your little trap but not anymore!"

Baby's Daddy: "Okay, so now you think you're clever because you have a job!"

Julya: "This job doesn't pay enough to cover all of my bills! You have it twisted. I'm not trying to get pregnant again over some irresponsible act."

Baby's Daddy: "Okay, let's go somewhere and talk about this."

Julya: "Okay, there you go again, trying to go somewhere so you can try something! I don't want to sit down and talk about it. I want you to stop coming over my house at late hours and disrespecting me and the kids. I don't have to answer my door at some late hours because you feel horny. Don't try to use the money as an excuse. I'm not feeling you anymore but you need to do what you know is right. You got too many women on the side and I'm trying to move on with my life and I'll find someone who really cares and will be right for me without any strings attached."

Baby's Daddy: "Just take the fucking money and let's go to your place and do what you like! You know you miss me!"

Julya: "I don't miss you because you'll do that and you'll move on to the next victim! You don't have a patent on that thing between your legs. I can get that elsewhere and I'm not selling out to get it!"

Baby's Daddy: "Okay, be gone, you wench! I'll see you soon!"

The baby's daddy walks off and gets into his car. He aggressively drives off.

Julya makes a phone call to her pastor and leaves a message. "Pastor Danig, can you please call me at your earliest convenience?"

Scene: At the airport with Maylee. They are at the security checkpoint and are saying goodbye for now. He hugs and kisses her and walks out to the parking structure. While walking, he notices a message on his cellphone. He then calls Julya while he's driving from the airport:

Pastor Danig: "Well, hello, Julya, I got your message, what's going on?"

Julya: "Well, Pastor, I think my problem is worse than I thought earlier because my baby's daddy followed me to the grocery store."

Pastor Danig: "What?"

Julya: "Yes, he met me in the parking lot and gave me the money he tried to give me last night."

Pastor Danig: "He followed you to a grocery store parking lot to give you child support money? That doesn't sound like a bad thing!"

Julya: "Pastor, please listen to me! He wanted to have sex! After he gave me the envelope, he asked me if I wanted to go back to my place. I told him no and he gave me the money anyway, called me a wench and then drove off erratically."

Pastor Danig: "Okay, so you think you're in danger, Julya?"

Julya: "Yes, because like I was telling you before, he had that look in his eye like he was up to something. I think he might try to come over later."

Pastor Danig: "Well, you don't have to answer the door."

Julya: "If he sees my car, he will hang around and wait for me. I don't have time for this type of pressure and I just need peace of mind. I wish he didn't know where I lived because I don't want to see him at all."

Pastor Danig: "It really sounds like you need to go to court and have an arrangement for how the child support is paid. You also need to get a restraining order if you feel this guy is endangering your life. I'm sorry that you're mixed up with a person who's the father of your children and who seems to pose a danger to you."

Julya: "Can I call you if he shows up?"

Pastor Danig: "You should call the police. I don't want to get mixed up in this problem. The best thing for you to do is contact the police if he's hanging around where you live. He is basically harassing or stalking you and you don't have to deal with this."

"If he shows up, I'm going to call the police and then I'll call you because I need the support, please."

Pastor Danig: "If you need to call me, that's fine but make sure you call the police and you might consider just going down to the station and just completing the paperwork for a restraining order now. If he makes you feel unsafe and you've told him time and time again that you don't want him near you, then it is your right to do so. Anyway, I must go, Julya, I have another call coming in."

Julya: "Okay, Pastor, I'll call you later."

Pastor Danig clicks over:

Scene: It's his wife calling from the airport:

Maylee: "Hey, I'm about to board the plane and I just wanted to hear your voice before we took off."

Pastor Danig: "Okay, sweetie, let me just say a short prayer with you before we hang up. Lord, we pray that you allow for a safe flight across the airways. I also pray that my mother-in-law's health gets better and that whatever the affliction is that you have the answer and the power to heal. I'm praying that you give us the strength to understand each other in this marriage and help us endure some of the problems."

Maylee: "Thank you for that prayer! It was a beautiful and needed prayer!"

Pastor Danig: "Have a safe trip and please call me as soon as you land."

Maylee: "Take care, dear, and I love you."

Pastor Danig: "I love you, too. Goodbye."

Scene: Young church couple who have attended for several years:

Tony and Beatrice are a couple in their mid-20s and married at the church where they currently attend. They faithfully tithed since they joined the church and are excited about the ministry. Their marriage seems to be the perfect marriage from his perspective.

Tony: "Hey, honey, let's go to Bible study tonight."

Beatrice: "Do we have to go tonight? I want to spend some time with my husband!"

Tony: "Well, we can spend time after the Bible study! It's going to be really good and the deacon told me that he really wants to see us there tonight!"

Beatrice: "Okay, well, I guess we'll still have time to spend being that it's Wednesday and you have to get up at 5 in the morning."

Tony: "Bible study is only for an hour and a half and we should be home by 9! That's plenty of time for us to spend time and we'll be together at the Bible study anyway."

Beatrice: "I guess and I hope it's only an hour and a half! You know how they get sometimes at the end when they start playing music and people, including you, honey, start hanging around at the end and talking to everybody"

Tony: "Okay, sweetheart, I promise that I won't hang around talking to everybody! We'll make this night special and leave immediately!"

Beatrice laughed and said, "Okay, I will guarantee that you won't be able to get up and leave when it's over!"

Tony: "Okay, let's make a bet and whoever wins the bet gives the other a 30-minute full-body massage when we get home."

Beatrice: "Okay, I know I'm going to win this one so you might as well get the oil and bathtub ready because I want it to be done right!"

Tony laughs and insists that he will win this bet: "Okay, since you know how the full-body massage works, I'll be looking forward to your best service!"

Beatrice: "Okay, I can't wait to win!"

Scene: At the church parking lot:

Tony and Beatrice pull up at the parking lot in their Chevrolet Corsica and the parking attendant directed them to park in an empty space. Beatrice gets out of the car and the parking attendant stares at her quickly hoping that her husband wouldn't notice. Beatrice noticed that he looked at her and she played it off as it was nothing. Beatrice knows that she's an attractive lady and it is not uncommon that men and even women give her compliments from time to time.

The parking attendant smiled and said, "Praise the Lord, beautiful couple!"

They responded, "Praise the Lord," and proceeded to walk into the sanctuary.

As they walked into the vestibule, they were greeted by some of the ushers and other members. The young handsome couple easily stood out because they had such outgoing personalities and were very excited about their new walk with the Lord. During church services, they are usually seen standing and yelling out "Yes" and "Amen" whenever the preacher said something provocative or maybe not so provocative.

Background on Tony: He was a loving husband and finally found what he knew was his soulmate. His previous relationships had been with women who used him and took advantage of his kindness. He did all that he could to please the women in his life but even as it related to the bedroom, it might not have been adequate enough for a nymphomaniac, which were the types he dated. Those relationships never lasted and the common response at the demise of the relationship was they would tell him that they weren't ready for commitment.

Background on Beatrice: She is the same type of woman that Tony has dated in the past. She is a nymphomaniac but is very skilled at putting on the façade that she is dedicated to one man. Whenever she sees a woman that seems to be loose, she criticizes that woman and even uses scripture reference to act like she's deep and far from doing this. However, her mind is always lusting after other men and women. She watches excessive TV and fantasizes about other men and dreams of one day doing a ménage-a toi.

Scene: At the end of Bible Study:

The preacher has concluded Bible study and the closing music begins. Everyone slowly exits the building and as Tony makes an attempt with his wife to leave, one of his friends runs up to him and starts talking about a gospel concert that they wanted to carpool with other friends. He tells his friend, "Hey, cool, man, let's talk about it later! I'm in a hurry! I'll call you later!"

He continues walking and his wife is in his shadow as they try to make it out into the lobby of the church. Before they can get out, they are accosted by the deacon and his wife. They are smiling and the deacon begins speaking to Tony.

"Hey, Tony, I'm so glad you made it out to Bible study tonight! I would really like to talk to you about getting involved in some teaching one of our youth Sunday school classes. I think it would be a perfect match for you and would love to talk to you about this right now in my office, please."

Tony looks at his wife with the knowledge that he's on his way to losing the bet and she smirks while saying, "I want my massage!" Tony hesitates and then realizes that he will have to lose this bet because he desired working with the youth and was eager to see what the deacon had to say.

Beatrice said in a long drawn-out sarcastic voice, "Go ahead, I'll wait out here for you!"

The excited deacon said, "I promise, we won't be long!"

Beatrice smiled and walked over to the table where there were books and CDs of previous Bible studies. As she looked at the different media forms, the parking attendant who had left his post to go to the restroom noticed Beatrice in the lobby looking at media and decided to walk up to her a pay another compliment.

Parking Attendant: "You look great and your husband is a lucky man being married to someone like you!"

Beatrice: "Well, thanks for the compliment and I think it's more than looks that makes it work!"

Parking Attendant: "I bet!" He smiles and starts imagining what she might have meant by such a statement. His mind was on sexual matters and was willing to accept the challenge by risk flirting with her to see if there was any sign of weakness in her marriage. He continued and said, "Well, really don't know what you mean by that statement but I bet it must be good in all areas! I'm jealous and I wish I had that!"

He then winks at her and she laughs and says, "Okay, well, the Lord will work it out for you!"

Parking Attendant: "I think he already has!" and then winks his eye. He walks off and then she wonders in her mind what he was talking about.

Scene: *The couple is in their car on the way home from Bible Study:*

As Tony and Beatrice are driving home, thunderstorms could be heard in the distance and large raindrops sparsely drop on the windshield and then moments later the rain started to pour down intensely to the point that the windshield wipers were ineffective. Tony decided to pull the car over to the side of the road until the rain subsided. While they sat in the car and waited for the intense rain to subside, Tony began sharing what occurred in the meeting.

Tony was excited and said, "You know, I have so much to tell you about the meeting! I thought he wanted me to just teach the youth Sunday school but the deacon wants me to consider being the youth minister. He even suggested that I talk it over with you before I make the decision. They are really about family in this ministry to even say something like that!"

Beatrice said with surprising sarcasm, "Minister? Since when did you become remotely interested in becoming a minister?"

Tony: "Well, sweetheart, you know that we are all ministers! Stop acting like you don't know what we learned in our Bible classes!"

Beatrice: "Well, not that type of minister! We can minister to others with what we know about the word but you're trying to be a minister over a set group of youth and that is an enormous responsibility! Do you think you're ready for something like that?"

Tony, in his excitement, said, "I think this might be the plan of God in my life! Sometimes we don't know until stuff starts happening and you know I'm great with the kids! Also, it is a ministry position that pays $22,000 a year and the deacon told me I can still work my day job! I think the only problem might be some of our quality time will be less but we can make up for it by going on really nice vacations that we can now afford, I might add!"

Beatrice: "Well, pray about this one because the extra money sounds good but you don't even know what the position involves nor do you know how much time you're going to be away from home. Did you at least talk to the person that was in that position before they fired him?"

Tony: "Fired?"

Beatrice: "Yes, fired!"

Tony: "How did you know about that?"

Beatrice: "Well, I heard through a reliable source that the other youth minister was holding separate offerings and using the money for his own personal gain. Rumor has it that he used it for the down payment on that BMW that he's driving but don't mix me up with all of that gossip! I just know that he took those kids' money! They were paying him a decent salary and he stole from those kids so he could pimp himself out! He was so into himself and hardly let the kids get involve with anything—he did all of the talking and had them little girls running behind him because he thought he was the greatest gift to mankind!"

Tony: "Baby, it sounds like you're gossiping now and who told you this?"

Beatrice ignored the latter part of Tony's question and responded to his gossiping assertion. "No, I'm just giving you the low-down of what I heard because you're going to be in the same position and I don't want my husband getting mixed up in a bunch of foolishness! I hope that if you accept this position that you will not get the big head because these kids seem to put a lot of trust in these youth pastors and the treat them like rock stars."

Tony: "I'm not going to be like that! That isn't even my personality! In fact, I'm sure those kids are going to have their guard up especially after they have been betrayed by their former leader."

Beatrice: "I don't think so. Those youth don't even know why he left. They covered it up really well and they think he left because he had another job opportunity."

The rain subsided a little and the street markings became slightly visible again. The steady rain still required the wipers to be on the fastest speed but Tony felt it was safe to start driving again. As he drives, he says to Beatrice, "Well, I'm not going to worry about what someone else did that was so wrong. In fact, I'm going show them that there are some good people out there who aren't in it to manipulate or take advantage of people."

Beatrice: "I'm sure that's what the other minister might have thought until those kids started treating him like he was bigger than life! Anyway, I'm looking forward to my massage! You lost this one fair and square!"

Tony: "No, that shouldn't count because it was like a job interview! Did you notice how I was walking out of the church and everyone that came up to me did not cause me to stop until I got to the deacon?"

Beatrice: "Don't try to change the rules. You lost this one fair and square and you might as well forget about trying to negotiate your way out of this one!"

Tony was so excited about the opportunity that he didn't mind losing and told Beatrice, "I'm going to hook you up real good like an experienced masseuse."

Scene: It is 5:15 in the morning and Tony is preparing to go to his day job at the call center at a cellular company:

Tony: "Beatrice, I'm going to be leaving the job a little early because I need time to get to the orientation, which starts at 3 P.M. I'll be going straight to the church!"

As Beatrice peaks her head out of the blanket, she says, "So you've already made your decision? I thought we were going to talk about this."

Tony: "We talked about it last night and you acted like it was okay. Anyway, we'll see what happens; the orientation is going to really show what the position is all about." He leans over to kiss her on the forehead and grabs his keys from the table next to the reading lamp. "I'll let you know when I get home! Don't cook anything because I won't get home until around 9 or so."

Tony heads out and gets in the car and starts playing his favorite gospel songs. He starts singing the words in the wrong key but the music is so loud that it isn't noticeable. As he's driving en route to the job he pulls into Dunkin' Donuts. He jumps out of the car and heads into the store and orders a coffee and a Boston Kreme.

As he's waiting for the worker to prepare his coffee, one of the church members runs up to him and asks, "Are you the new youth minister?"

Tony: "Well, not yet, I'm going to find out about the position later today."

The lady was excited and said, "Well, I hope you get the position because I've seen you and you wife around the church and you seem like such a nice couple!"

Tony: "Well, thanks and if I see you again, I'll let you know if I got it or not!"

"Well, I'm sure we might see each other again being that I go to the church and my daughter is part of the youth group."

As Tony is paying for his coffee and donut, he then says, "Okay, we'll see you soon then!" and then he grabs the change, receipt, and a napkin.

He gets in his car and starts heading toward the job, which is about a mile down the street in a business park. He finishes his donut and then walks in the call center and punches in with the coffee on his left hand and the card in his right hand. He then takes a seat next the call station next to where his college buddy, Rob, is seated.

He logs in the computer and Rob says, "What's going on, man, and what's the good word for the day?"

Tony: "Well, the good word is that I might be the new youth minister. I'm going to find out by the end of today, that's why I have to leave a little early today."

His friend raises his eyebrow and says, "Wow, that sounds interesting. When did you decide to become a minister? I mean, I hear you talking about church all of the time and blasting gospel music but minister?"

Tony: "You sound like my wife. She said the same thing and yes, minister. They want me to be the youth minister."

"Wow," said Rob. "So now are we going to get you quoting scriptures up in here?"

Tony: "Very funny! I think I do a little of that now!"

Rob: "So what does your wife think about all of this?"

"She seems to be cool with it." Tony places the headset and mouthpiece on his head as he gets ready to start taking calls.

Rob says, "Man, your wife doesn't even seem like the type that would be all up in the church world!"

Tony: "Well, she is and you certainly can't go by looks these days."

Rob: "Yeah, man, I ain't trying to be disrespectful but your wife is a dime piece! Do you ever have problems with people trying to spit game at that?"

Tony: "I'm sure people will try to do that spitting game, as you call it, but I trust my wife to shut it down before it gets out of control."

Rob: "Yeah, I feel you, man, but I don't trust people out there. Your wife might be strong enough to shut it down but some people know the game and are good at pushing themselves on fine woman."

Tony: "Well, I'm not going to walk around worrying about stuff like that because we have great communication and if anyone crossed the line with my wife, she would share it with me and then we can deal with it from there. I'm not going to sit around worrying about it, though!" Tony then takes the call and says, "This is Tony, how can I be of excellent service to you?"

The person on the line started arguing about why the phone company turned off their phone over a $5.00 balance. The angry customer said, "I paid all of my bill except $5.00 and they turned my phone off. This is ridiculous and an emergency situation could have occurred!"

Tony: "Okay, sir, the way the system is set up is if you don't pay the entire bill, the system will automatically disconnect the service even if it is something as low as $5.00. However, if you call in advance and make an arrangement on paying a portion of the bill, then we can stop the system for disconnecting you over the remaining balance. I will restore your service and put the remaining balance toward your next bill."

The angry customer said, "With all of this technology, you mean the computer could not have done this in the first place?"

Tony: "Okay, sir, I understand your frustration and apologize for the inconvenience. For now, I'll restore the service and if you would like, I can forward you to our customer relations department, where you can voice your concerns in an attempt to better our service."

The angry customer said, "I ain't got time for that, you can tell them that they need to change the system so it doesn't cut people's phones off over a small balance that's due! This is ridiculous!"

Tony: "I'll make note of it, and is there anything else I can help you with today, sir?"

"No, that's it!"

"Okay," replies Tony. "Now sir, sometimes it takes a couple of minutes for the system to restore your phone. If your phone isn't working when we complete this call, simply turn it off and wait a couple of minutes and then turn it on again."

Scene: Later that evening at around 10 P.M.:

Tony walks in the door and is greeted by his wife with a hug.

Beatrice: "How did your day go?"

Tony: "It was great. I met with Pastor Danig and the other ministers and deacons and they basically asked me a few questions about being a minister. It seemed like an interview, which I didn't prepare for but I think that's what they wanted. They all sat around in a casual sense and asked me all sorts of questions but it wasn't consecutive. One would ask a questions and after I answered it, another would start talking about something in the ministry, which led to the next question. It was like they each had their own question for me. What was good about the interview was at the end they all shook my hand and welcomed me to the ministerial staff. I felt like I just walked into a door of opportunity. Honey, I feel that God has called me into this and is directing my path."

Beatrice looks at him in amazement as if she cannot believe what he's saying and the responds with a fake excitement, "That sounds great!" Tony doesn't realize that she really isn't genuinely excited and then proceeds to talk about the job functions but is interrupted by Beatrice, "Honey, let's relax and talk about something else—you've been gone all day and I think I should tell you about my day."

Tony: "Okay, I'm sorry—I was so excited about how the day went until I forgot to ask you how your day went!"

Beatrice: "It was boring and I missed you."

Tony: "You know, honey, I love you so much and I missed you, too! You don't know how happy I am to be married to a wife who loves the Lord as I do. I think this ministry thing is going to be good for our marriage even though I might be a bit busier but I'll make sure that I won't allow my busy schedule to interfere with our quality time."

Beatrice smiles and walks toward the kitchen and asks him, "Are you hungry?"

Tony: "No, they fed us all day basically—I mean there was just so much good food that was prepared by the mothers of the church just sitting there waiting to be eaten! I know it was some good eating and I wish you were there to help me eat some of that homecooked food!"

Beatrice said with a smile and a little sarcasm, "Sounds nice but I'm hungry and I'm going to eat some of my homecooked leftovers!"

She then put something in the toaster-oven and while it was heating started putting some salad in a small bowl. She added grapes to the salad and then in a playful manner decided to throw a grape at Tony while he sat in the dining area scrolling through papers. The impact of the grape on his forehead splattered grape juice on some of the papers and Tony responded, "Honey, I have to sign these papers and return them and now they have grape juice stains! I don't want to turn these documents in with grape stains, it's unprofessional!"

Beatrice starts laughing and then said, "Relax, they've already chosen you for the job and grape stains aren't going to change that! In fact, you can tell them that we were making wine and while we were smashing grapes some of the juice splashed on your papers. Didn't Jesus turn water to wine?" She continued laughing and then continued, "Let's make some wine, Tony! Come on and have a little fun, even Jesus knew how to have a little fun!"

Tony: "You play too much and I'm not playing right now!"

Scene: Six months later and Tony and Beatrice are at home on a Saturday evening on the couch watching a rental movie. This is the first time they were able to sit down and watch something at home together. Tony was too tired to try to take his wife to a movie or music event and they decided to just stay home and watch a movie:

Beatrice: "Tony, you're finally home! We can sit and watch a movie together!" Beatrice was not that disappointed in them not spending lots of time together and she went on to say, "I know that your schedule is really busy now and I thought I would have a problem with it but it seems that I appreciate the time we spend together even though it is less than before."

Tony: "I must agree," as he stared aimlessly into the TV screen. He started to doze off while Beatrice continued talking.

Beatrice: "Honey, you know me and the girls are going to go out to hang out tomorrow after church, just to let you know."

Tony: "Sure, honey, you need to get out with your friends," he said with a slow speech as he began dozing off on the couch.

Beatrice realized that he was too tired to really continue the conversation while the movie was going on and decided to watch the movie alone.

Scene: Sunday evening moments before midnight and Beatrice returns home from visiting her friends:

As she enters the door, her husband is fast asleep on the couch. She walks straight into the bathroom in their bedroom and jumps in the shower. She comes out in her nightgown and tries to wake Tony. She realizes he's too tired to want to do anything but she tries anyway.

He says, "Honey, can we wait until tomorrow? I am way too tired and won't be any good!"

Beatrice: "I'll do all of the work, all you have to do is just lie there!"

"No," insisted Tony. "I'll be no good to you even lying there!"

She politely backed off and said, "Well, you need to get in the bed and get some real sleep because you have to get up in five hours!"

Tony: "It's that late? I can't believe it!"

He jumps off of the couch and rushes to the bed. Beatrice remains on the couch and begins channel surfing.

Scene: Two years later at their first new home:

Tony is in the backyard with some of his friends and is standing over the grill flipping burgers and chicken. They are talking about a minister who was fired for cheating on his wife with one of the members of the church. Tony said to his friends while he continued working the grill, "The board members felt it was in the best interest of the church to let him go. They mentioned his multiple indiscretions but this last woman called him out when she thought he would leave his wife and of course, he didn't leave his wife and she exposed him."

His friend Rob responded, "What's the deal with these ministers who go in the sacred places and cheat on their wives with members in the church? That's why I can't do church, because there are too many hypocrites!"

Tony: "Man, you can't let that stop you from being in church! The world is full of hypocrites and just because some are in the church, it doesn't make the church a bad place—it's just the people who need to be fixed and the church is the best place to help them."

Rob responded, "Well, it seems awfully strange that the people who act like they are the authorities on helping people with problems are the ones who have the biggest problems. I don't get people who call themselves leaders in the church are found messing with people's wives and having affairs. That is not acceptable and then everyone wants to try to keep it quiet so they can protect the interest of the church." Rob continues, "Man, please tell me what the best interest of the church means, I mean that sounds like some type of scheme."

Tony: "No one is above reproach."

Rob: "No one is above reproach? Can you break that down in layman's terms, what is reproach?"

Tony: "Rebuke."

Rob: "Keep breaking it down."

Tony: "Okay, no one is above being criticized for doing something wrong."

Rob: "Then why do these church leaders act like they are above doing something wrong?"

Tony: "Well, some people have fallen because they were weak in the flesh and have not studied the word, fasted, or prayed. They became weak after they were initially strong."

Rob: "You still didn't answer my question on what is the best interest of the church."

Tony: "Well, it's what we're talking about right now and it's about the perception of the church! People get the wrong idea about church when they see the leaders doing wrong things and so to protect the church from such negative imagery, they let people go who taint the image of the church. So it is in the best interest of the church to either sit people down in leadership or counsel them."

Rob: "Okay, so you mentioned how people start off strong and then become weak—now here is a scenario for you. Suppose you used to be a womanizer and then you got delivered from that. You are now strong and then you decide to get married and have promised that you will keep your vows and be faithful to your wife. Several years down the road, you start working with someone in your workplace and become attracted to that person and then it escalates to something that will betray your marriage to your wife. How do you explain when the person believed they were delivered from the womanizing lifestyle?"

Tony: "Well, they were never delivered!"

Rob: "Come on, man, they must have been delivered at least for some point in time because they managed to be truthful for a few years until the temptation overwhelmed them."

Tony: "That's the problem, the temptation overwhelmed the person and they weren't in the word the way they needed to be so they fell."

Rob: "Well, I still don't get it. I think ministers and deacons need to be so much to the level that they are not falling for temptations! They want to lead people and that comes with a big price tag! I think if you are trying to lead people spiritually, you have to be the type of person that isn't lustful and it seems that these leaders have this problem. They lust for women, men, money, and things!"

Meanwhile Beatrice is in the kitchen talking to the wives and girlfriends of Tony's friends. Beatrice's close friend, Raquel, is sitting to her left and the other girlfriends are sitting around the table.

"So Beatrice," says one of the other girls, "it seems like you and Tony have a really good marriage."

Beatrice: "Yeah, things are cool."

One of her friends says, "Well, you don't sound so sure!"

Beatrice: "Well, we have a good marriage but Tony is so busy with his day job and his job as a youth minister—we hardly have time together. But it is good in one sense because when we are together, we really appreciate being in each other's company. We have lots of fun and I think it is better this way because we don't really argue much or overdose on each other."

One of the girls says, "Uh-huh," as if she was acknowledging something good that a preacher said from the pulpit.

Beatrice went on to say, "You know what I mean! Sometimes when you're around someone too much, you start to get on each other's nerves and end up arguing over stupid stuff."

Raquel: "I hear you, my man and me are fight a lot over stupid stuff! I remember we argued fiercely for an hour straight and then we apologized and then we had good sex. When we were done with the sex, we lied in the bed and asked each other, what were we arguing about? We both didn't have a clue—we simply could not remember what started the argument or what we were arguing about!"

Beatrice: "Maybe it was the sex that threw it out of your minds!"

The girls started laughing.

One of the girls at the table asked, "Has anyone ever cheated on their husband or boyfriend?"

Beatrice, "Well, it depends on how you define cheating."

Raquel: "Well, going on a date with another man in my opinion is cheating or at least leading to cheating. Kissing another man on the mouth is cheating even if you don't have sex. That's my opinion on the matter and maybe I'm a little old fashioned but if you have any intimacy outside of sex with someone other than your partner, it is cheating. Your partner needs to know about any relationship you have with anyone and that will change the definition of cheating because they know what you're up to."

"Okay, so based on her definition of cheating, who cheated at this table?"

Everyone slowly raised their hands except the older friend who'd been married for a long time.

One of the girls at the table said, "So that makes us all tramps and whores."

Beatrice, "I ain't no whore but if I see something I like I still like the challenge to see if I can get the attention. I love attention and sometimes my husband doesn't give it to me. It just feels good to get it even though it can be innocent."

The other friend jumps in, "Okay, my definition of cheating is when you simply have some type of sex with someone and I mean oral, anal and vaginal. That's cheating to me! I don't think when you're in a relationship with someone that you should be sharing your body with someone unless your significant other is okay with it."

Beatrice stares at her as if she wanted to say something but then she continued on her definition. "If my man agreed to have an open relationship, I might be for it but I have to approve of the other person or I get to pick the woman. He's not picking the woman because if he picks her then he might like her more than me. I'm the one who gets to evaluate and pick the woman because I'll know that if he ends up liking her, I'll know that she won't be down for trying to get with him. So based on my definition, how many of you cheated on your significant other?"

No one raised their hands and then the friend said, "C'mon, y'all know you're lying because you raised your hand on the first time and don't worry, what we say here stays here."

All but Tamika, who had been married for seventeen years, raised their hands.

"Okay, well, we won't ask who y'all been slipping out with on the side but what makes a person want to get with another person after you already made a commitment to the person you claimed you love?"

Beatrice jumps in and says, "It's the excitement and the challenge. You're not even attached to the person you cheated with even though you connect with them in the sex act. It just feels good at the moment and you know it is something wrong and taboo, which makes the danger of it all that much better."

Tamika said, "I disagree strongly, you can't be sleeping with another person after you've committed yourself to one person. That is just blatant dishonesty and corruption!"

Beatrice: "Okay, sanctified momma, you do know that if you think something in your mind, it's just like doing the act and you can't tell me that you haven't fantasized about some other man whether he was on TV, in a grocery store or in your church? I just do what most people think about and then I'll ask for forgiveness! Am I lying or what?"

Tamika said, "No, I don't fantasize about other men because my husband is all I need for intimacy and any other needs. Fantasizing about another is a disloyal thought and if I'm living a sanctified life I don't need to fantasize about anything that is outside of my husband! But I don't need to do that since we can create things together in reality! And furthermore, the world is full of attractive people but you don't have to lust or covet after them."

Beatrice: "Well, I find that hard to believe and if that's true, I want whatever strength you have to just be stuck on one person!"

Tamika said, "I've been married for seventeen years and our relationship has gotten stronger over the years. I can't say that it was all perfect but when you stay in the word and both of you trust in God, things work out even when things get rough."

Beatrice then says, "Well, I've slipped up a couple times and this is the first time I ever shared it with anyone and I feel ashamed but at the same time I feel I cannot help my ways."

Tamika said, "Well, you should feel ashamed if you're doing acts against your marriage! Does your husband know?"

Beatrice: "Not yet."

Tamika: "Well, you're living a lie and that's not good for any marriage! You're going to have to tell him at some point. It isn't fair to him that you've betrayed the trust and then concealed it from him. If you really trust God, no matter how bad you think he may take it, you owe it to him and yourself to tell him the truth. He will be distraught probably and in a worst-case scenario leave you but he will respect you in the end for telling him. However, if you don't tell him and he finds out through another source, he will probably never respect you no matter the outcome."

Beatrice sits in silence for a minute and then one of the other girls changes the subject. "Hey, Beatrice, do you have any wine or something, I need to relax my nerves. All this cheating stuff is working on me."

Scene: Later that evening, after the guests leave:

Beatrice is walking around the house and picking up dishes and glasses from the living room and patio. She puts the dishes in the dishwasher and then calls her husband. He was in the bedroom and said, "I'll be out in a minute; I need to finish sending this email."

Beatrice says, "Okay, when you're done, I'll be in the living room."

Beatrice asks Tony to come into the living room so she could talk with him. She begins the conversation with, "Tony, I have something that I need to tell you and it is not good."

Tony said, "What's the matter, sweetie?"

"I need to tell you something that I've been struggling with for such a long time."

Tony: "Okay, you've been struggling with something for a long time? Why haven't you told me—anyway, what is it, sweetie?"

Beatrice said very quickly, "I want a divorce."

Tony dropped his phone and said, "Excuse me, you want a what?" He started trembling and Beatrice was surprised at his response as she never saw him behave so nervously.

Tears started running down her eyes as she continued, "I know I said that I would be there for you even when you got so involved in the ministry but I could not handle the attention that everyone seemed to be getting from you other than me."

Tony responded with disbelief in his voice, "I thought that you said that we were better together when we weren't in each other's faces all the time! Why didn't you tell me that I wasn't giving you enough attention and why are we talking about divorce? This is something that we can work out and you should even be talking about a divorce!"

Beatrice: "Well...."

He interrupts and says, "I'm sorry; I'll quit the minister position and this will give us more time together. I can put in for the manager position at the call center and if I get that, we will be okay with the bills."

Beatrice hurriedly responds, "No, no, no, don't quit anything!"

Tony: "But you said that I wasn't giving you enough attention and this ministry job is causing me to not give you enough attention! I'll call them up right now because I don't want you to leave me!"

Beatrice said, "Let me finish explaining why I want a divorce and it is not only because of you not giving me enough attention! I only told you part of the reason why I want a divorce."

She pauses for a moment and he then asks her, "What's going on, Beatrice? You're scaring me, honey, please tell me what's going on!"

Tony tries to reach out and hug Beatrice but she backs off. She responds, "You're not going to want to touch me or be with me after I tell you what I have been doing for the past three years."

Tony: "Three years?"

Beatrice says with a solemn voice: "Yes, three years."

Tony's hands were shaking nervously and Beatrice became more reluctant to tell him the details of the truth and said, "I just don't want to be in this marriage anymore! I've been faking it all of these years and I don't want to fake it anymore! I just don't think we were meant to be together."

Tony cries out, "Will you please stop being so general about this and tell me what's going on! I can handle it but what I can't handle is more lies, so you might as well tell me the truth, please!"

Beatrice paused for a moment and asked him, "Please sit down, your shaking is scaring me."

Tony then sits and says, "Please tell me what's going on, Beatrice?"

Beatrice: "Okay, I slept with four different people in the last two and a half years."

Tony looked at her in astonishment as if he was dreaming. He didn't say anything but the look in his eyes epitomized his world crashing. He held his head down for a moment and then stared at her as she began to give the details.

Beatrice: "The first person I got involved worked at the church and was the parking attendant who was always complimenting me. He told me that he thought I was beautiful and made it seem like it was a challenge of a lifetime to be with me. I knew I was married but he told me that I could be his man on the side and that no one would know. I fell for this lie because he was an attractive man and I have a lustful problem when I see a good-looking man. So while you were working in youth ministry, I fell into the arms of another man. I would have never thought that a church worker would dare think of such a challenge. He was charming and looked very handsome outside of his security uniform. Anyway, I was having an affair with him for a year until he left to go out of state for a state job in Oregon. I haven't heard from him since."

Tony: "I don't believe this! You're saying this so nonchalantly as if you would continue to deal with him if he didn't move out of state. I can't believe you were sleeping with someone and then having sex with me! I thought we were married and that you loved me only!"

Beatrice: "Just wait, please let me finish! I might as well tell you everything since I'm leaving anyway. Nothing I do or say is going to change that and just to let you know, the things I did had nothing to do with what you weren't doing. I have this affliction that I never really been delivered from even though I thought I was, I could never really tame the demons that torment me to be with different people."

Tony: "I'm supposed to be a minister and you're telling me that demons tormented you and I was never able to discern this and you never reached out to me as my wife to tell me this!"

Beatrice: "I must finish telling you the rest. The next person was your colleague at the call center. You invited him over when we had the 'get-together' with your friends. You didn't notice but he was staring at me through the entire get-together. He got my number somehow from the computers at your job. He called me and said that he thought I was attractive and wanted to show me what it was like when a man worshipped a beautiful body such as mine. It was a one-night stand and it wasn't how he bragged it would be, he simply pumped away like a machine. The third infidelity occurred with one of the ministers that you work with. He was the minister that you and you buddies were talking about that got fired for sleeping with that white girl. He was involved with me before he even thought of that other girl and it was easy to sneak around because he knew where you'd be. In fact, he was the one who helped get you the youth minister job so that he could get to me. The last person I was involved with was Minister Galvin's wife. She likes men and women. She invited me over to her house and they partied like nothing I've ever witnessed, especially church folks. They played loud music, drank, did cocaine and got me involved with a ménage-a toi, something I've always wanted to do. The only problem is that I dreamt of two men rather than two women. So I did it with the minister and his wife and she opened me up some sexual fantasies that I never imagined. It was the best sexual experience of my life! I want a divorce because I don't want to live this married life anymore. I like the lifestyle of having experiences with different people. People weren't meant to be with one person. Take a look around you, so many people are cheating because it is unnatural to be with one person."

Tony: "Okay, now I know that you must be joking and this isn't my wife talking! Why are talking so much about sexual stuff? Our sex wasn't good enough!"

Beatrice: "No, I'm not and I'm almost finished, so please listen!" she said with strong emphasis. "I've been untruthful to you from the beginning and I thought I would grow out of my affliction but I'm not and I don't even want to! It's not for me and I'm sorry that I led you to believe that I was here for you."

Tony remained silent and dumfounded by the events that he had absolutely no clue about. Beatrice had already had her suitcase packed and it was lying in the midst.

She reached over to pick it up and Tony said to her, "I can't believe that I can still talk to you after what I've heard, but where are you going?"

Beatrice: "I'm just leaving you, Tony." She started crying while she was fumbling to get her suitcase.

Tony held his hands out as if he was reaching out to help her and she was too involved with getting her things that she did not look at him anymore. "Just like that! You're just walking away after spilling out all of this bad news and not telling me where you're going or who you're running off with?"

Beatrice: "I told you all that I needed to tell you!" She grabbed her suitcase and headed out the door.

Tony: "You can't just walk away like this!"

She brushed past him and stormed out of the door and got in the cab that was already parked alongside the curve adjacent to the house. Tony stood in silence and disbelief and started crying while staring at their wedding pictures on the entertainment center.

Scene: The next day at Tony and Beatrice's home:

It's Monday morning and Tony lay in bed in a state of depression. He didn't show up to work nor did he call his job to let them know that he would not be coming in. His cellphone mailbox flashed green showing twenty-two missed calls. As he lay there in a state of depression, he fell in and out of sleep and began dreaming. Before he fell asleep, he laid there curled up in the bed like an infant needing comfort and protection from his mother but with only the blanket to cover him. His mind raced with so many thoughts of betrayal and deception. He tried thinking to God about his problems while intermittently yelling out, "Why?" Tony's thoughts:

"Lord, I did what I thought was your will and yet the one I loved betrayed my love. I don't understand what I did wrong. I thought I did what an honest and faithful husband should do and yet the deception went on without me having a clue. I thought I would have had some type of warning or clue if something was wrong in my marriage. I don't know what to think. I am surrounded by the enemy. People in my workplace, my friends and the people at my church have let me down. I do not understand what I did wrong. Did I not please my wife intimately? I cannot understand why I continue to go through the same struggles. Before I got married, the women I dated pretended that they liked me and then they would betray me before ending the relationship. I know that I was not designed to continue suffering the same trial over and over again. What did I do wrong to have to have such a trial? Why didn't you tell me that the woman that I thought was my soulmate would do this to us? She led me to believe that she cared about me and that there was no other. I believed her and she never really complained about what I might have been doing wrong in the relationship. I was too naïve to see that a problem existed in my marriage because I was so caught up in my work and I trusted her completely. How did I not see the signs of trouble in my marriage? The enemy just came in took away what I thought was mine. God, what did I do wrong? Did love fail or did I fail?"

Tony then went into a deep sleep and began having a series of dreams. His dreams took him back to events in his childhood and then events in his adulthood. When he was 14 years old, he dreams of his cousins coming over during the summer break from school and all of them going to the roller skating rink. They all made bets that they would ask a girl to skate couples before leaving the rink that night. All of them were able to skate with a girl except Tony and all of them teased him about it on their way home from the skating rink. The older brother didn't say much and ended up stepping in when the teasing got out of control. He noticed his younger brother getting upset when they wouldn't let up on the teasing.

Tony's dream then transitioned to his adult life when he was a freshman in college and his college buddies and he sat around in the dining hall. He noticed a very attractive girl sitting at the table with her roommate. His roommate and friend suggested that he go over there and say something to her if he expected to see what the outcome would be. He then said to his friends, "I don't even know her and she might have a boyfriend."

"Look," his roommate said, "if she had a boyfriend, chances are she would be sitting eating dinner with her instead of her roommate and the only way to find out is to ask her. In fact, that's a good way to start off the conversation. Anyway, we're on a university campus and if this girl happens to have a boyfriend, just count your loss and move on. No one is serious about relationships on this campus anyway—mostly everybody is concerned about their grades in this expensive behind school. So go on over there and introduce yourself and see what you'll find out."

Tony said, "So you think I should just walk over there and start talking to a complete stranger?"

Roommate: "Yes, indeed! That's what we do here on a university campus. You have to socialize a bit and then go back to your studies. No one is going to get hurt, just introduce yourself and say a few things and then return to our table and tell us how it went. In fact, I am demanding that you do this since you are a freshman and this will be our way of initiating you to the campus life. So go for it."

Tony gets up and walks over and sits at the table. He looks at the girl that he's attracted to and asks her, "Do you mind if I sit here?"

She said, "No," and her roommate looked, smiled and said, "What is your name?"

Tony responded, "My name is Tony and I just thought I'd get to know people on this campus being that I am a freshman."

The girl that Tony was attracted to had dark brown eyes and curly blonde highlights that contrasted with her dark brown hair. She stared at him but said nothing but her roommate did all of the talking.

Tony asked her, "What's your name?"

She looked at him and said, "I don't just start talking to people I don't know and I didn't come to this campus to socialize with anyone."

Tony responded, "Well, I'm not just anyone and I might be in one of your classes because you're a freshman, aren't you?"

She said, "Yeah, I am and I'm in pre-med so I really don't have time to talk to anyone! Nothing personal but unless you're in any of my classes we don't have much to talk about."

Tony responded, "Well, it was nice talking to you, 'Miss Pre-med,' and I must be going!" He said with a bit of sarcasm, "It was a pleasure speaking to the both of you!" as he stared at the pretty girl's roommate. He walked off and headed toward the table where his roommate and friend sat.

His roommate said, "Oh, it doesn't look good, you've got that defeated look on your face."

They both laughed and then Tony said, "She was a snotty little angry little thing but I did get her to tell me her major. I never got the name, though."

Tony's dream then switches to the interview that he had with the minister who interviewed him for the youth minister position and who later slept with his wife. He remembers how reassuring he was about him getting the youth minister position. As they sat in the office and went over a few things, he would ask questions about their marriage and how things were on the home-front. Tony thought the minister was trying to get information about his marriage life so that he could see if he was the best candidate for the youth minister job. However, the minister had other motives and wanted to see if there was weakness so that he could move in on his wife. As Tony recalls the events in his dreams, he noticed how the minister insisted that he would have the wife's cell-phone number. He said that this was necessary because they wanted to talk with her and ask simple questions about the character of her husband. It was simple procedure and although a bit strange, it was something that the ministry has been doing for many years. Tony's dream then switches to the parking attendant and he noticed that ridiculous devilish smile that he wore on his face every time his wife stepped outside of the car. In his dream he realized the covetous lustful dynamic that was taking place and probably noticed it when it occurred but never took it as anything too serious as his wife would always share instances when men would stare at her. She noticed it more than he did but Tony did not really care because he felt that those people can look, imagine, and admire all they want but he believed his wife was faithful and dedicated to him only.

When Tony awakens, he gets up and walks into the bathroom and looks in the mirror. He picks up the toothbrush and as he reaches for the toothpaste, he notices a note folded up behind the shaving cream. While he opens it, the phone is heard ringing in the background but he ignores the rings. The note is handwritten on purple notepad paper by Beatrice:

Tony: One day you will find this note and by the time you read it, I will already be gone. I am better at writing my thoughts down rather than sharing them with anyone, so you will get a chance to read my thoughts on things I should have told you in our marriage. As you already know, I am not the woman that I led you to believe and throughout my life I have been battling with a sexual addiction. It started when I was a young child when my older brother taught me things about sex when I was eight years old. One day, I walked in on him looking at some pornography magazines that he found hidden in my parents' closet. I was confused because I didn't know why he was looking at magazines with naked people in them. He then told me that it was okay to look at the magazines because he said that Dad looked at them. He said he was trying to be like grownups and pleaded with me not to tell Dad that he snuck the magazines out of the closet. He asked me to promise to keep it a secret and that he would let me be like a grownup and look at the magazines with him and so I did. My father worked all of the time and it seemed like he was never home and so my brother went through his things and found the magazines and we would spend hours looking at these magazines. We would go into the basement and look at the magazines together and my brother would tell me things that grownups would do. He said that he saw Mom and Dad with no clothes on one day and they were making weird sounds. He then told me it is something that grownups do to have fun. He then said that he was going to sneak a girl that he said was his girlfriend over in the basement and show me what he saw Mom and Dad doing. So everything that happened in the basement that afternoon is so vivid in my mind. They both were 11 years old and I watched them have sex on the floor. He then told me not to tell anyone and that one day he was going to introduce me do a boy so that I could learn how to do it. I was scared at the time but he said it would be okay. I trusted my big brother and in my mind knew that he wouldn't let anything bad happen to me and that day came when I had sex with some boy he said was his friend and I was 10 years old and he was 13. I remember my brother telling me that it was lots of fun to do it but my first experience wasn't fun. It didn't feel like anything fun but it was a new experience being with a body. I didn't want to get pregnant because I heard of young girls getting pregnant and the parents sending them away. I didn't want my parents to know that I was having sex and I didn't want to get pregnant and be sent away. My big brother told me not to worry because I wasn't on my period and he said that when I do get my period he said to have anal sex. My brother and I became so good at sneaking around and concealing things from our parents. In fact, it was easy to do because both my parents were too busy to really pay attention to what we were doing. They did not have a clue that we were having sex. So as you can see, I was introduced to sex at a very young age and ever since then, it seems like it is so ingrained in me to want to do this with different people. I'm also good at hiding information just like I did when I was a child. I'm not satisfied being with one person. This strange addiction I have is like someone being addicted to drugs but mine is sex with different people. I can't be with one person. I'm sorry, Tony, but what we had intimately was good but it wasn't enough for me. I'm sorry that I kept this from you and that I cheated on you. I loved you for the person that you are but I did not love you enough to share my innermost secrets and fears. I feared that if I told you about my problem that you would help me get it fixed but I didn't want it to be fixed. I'm addicted to what I do and I don't want to change it. I'm sorry that you spent four years of your life with a stranger because that's what I was to you. It was never real. You were simply a portion of my addiction and as harsh as it sounds, that's my reality.

I decided to move to a state where none of my family or friends live. I was able to save money in order to make this move. I am sorry for what I did to you. Beatrice

Tears welled up in Tony's eyes and he then begins to wonder who to blame for this. He blames Beatrice for deceiving him. He blames the minister for sleeping with his wife. He blames God for not showing him a sign that he was being deceived. He blames himself for not discerning. He then starts to question salvation. Tony felt that he had an anointing in his life and that he had a close walk with God. He would pray and speak in tongues from time to time when under the anointing. He felt that he was in tuned with God and that the church was the environment for him for his spiritual connection as well as dealing with some of the emotional problems that he had growing up. Tony viewed the church as a place of refuge for his problems. He had emotional challenges that he felt he was delivered from but they resurfaced at the moment he was betrayed by his wife. All he thought he was delivered from now tormented him because he relied on his wife and the seeming success of his marriage as the measuring stick to his deliverance.

In his confused state, Tony decided to write a response to Beatrice's letter and not knowing if he would ever see her again, it would be his means to release the energy on paper. Perhaps one day she might get a chance to read his thoughts. As Tony feels betrayed, he feels a sense of incompleteness as Beatrice suddenly walked away without his feelings being heard.

Tony writes:

> *Dear Beatrice, You don't know how you've ripped my heart out. I feel like I'm in a forest with no compass and no place to go. I feel a sense of hopelessness because the ones that I thought were close to me have betrayed me. I thought you were everything and the one who completed me. I thought the church was my safe place and a place where I could be nurtured and protected from insolence. Well, since you shared with me some of your childhood experiences, I don't have much more to say other than what I told you already about my childhood. I thought we shared so much about ourselves to each other but you revealed some things to me that make me realize that you are not completely at fault for your actions. If you ever get a chance to read this letter, I want you to know that I still love you despite the pain I feel. I feel betrayed and angry even to the point of wanting to do harm to the people who abused and hurt you. My greatest fear was to know that the woman I loved would leave me for another. That fear has become a reality and I'm living this fear right now. I don't know if having such fear brought about the results but all I know is that it happened and I am here and you are somewhere unknown. Now you've shared some childhood experiences that shaped you to who you are today so, when I was a child, I was sheltered from the things you were exposed to. I didn't know about any adult things until I became an adult by our modern-day society's standards. During my childhood, having a girlfriend was a major event and it might have involved holding the girl's hand or going as far as a kiss. The adult world was brought into your life at an early age but the nymphomania that you experience is*

something different but I cannot analyze the situation because we aren't together anymore. It seems so strange and I am hurt beyond what words on a paper can articulate.

Right now the feeling that is at the forefront is betrayal. I am the type of man that feels validated as a man when my wife is linked to me solely. When this did not happen, it simply means betrayal. I never dreamed of having to share my wife with another but it happened and without me knowing. I don't even understand the nature of vows in a marriage if they cannot even be upheld. I don't understand why we got married if your lifestyle was against this. And the people in the church who were instrumental in counseling and supporting the institution of marriage in our lives were also instrumental in destroying it.

I prayed daily, fasted and did God's work. I remember a preacher saying that if I handled God's business, he would take care of my business. I don't understand how God would allow something like this to happen. Will God reveal something to me later regarding this trial in my life? I don't feel that I belong in the church anymore because the people there seem deceptive. I see them differently now. The smiles that I once embraced as sincere now have a diabolical and fake look to it. I see the people in the church a zombies walking around saying what sounds holy but not meaning a damn bit of what they say. The smiles are fake and the words that come out of their mouths are fake. The people in the church are fake zombies. They do what the preacher tells them to do and then they sneak around and do what they want to do. The church is a playground and a soap opera platform for people to play games and have sex and deceive each other. People get up in the morning and put on cologne and perfumes and wear fancy clothes to impress somebody. They go there looking good so they can get a mate or steal someone's mate. They don't care that they're in the church. I have been victimized by all of this.

I felt like giving up on life when you left me the way you did. I looked back on the events in our marriage and now I see clearly all of the corruption that occurred. This is after the fact but nevertheless, I see it. I see the fraud for what it is and it happened in a place that I least expected. The very people who guided me and nurtured me and led me are the same ones who stole from me in so many ways. They took the pain that I thought I was delivered from and magnified it many fold. I will never set foot in a church again because I see it for what it is. Every person who attends church is a fraud and why? Because they go for something. They're in it for something and that is fraudulent. They want something from God. They want something from man. They want a woman or a man. They want to hear music. They want to be seen by what they wear or what they do. They want someone to say a word to them so they can feel encouraged. That is fraudulent. Get your ass up and do something for yourself and stop waiting for someone else to do it for you. You are a fucking fraud, you fuck. Fuck you. Fuck you, Beatrice, you fraud. You tricked me just like everyone in my life. The people who say they are working for God tricked me. The wife who said she loved me tricked me. My friends, who called me friend, tricked me. I'm sick and fucking tired of all of the people in my life who tricked me. Fuck off and stay out of my life.

Scene: Pastor Danig arrives home:

He tells his children to wash their hands and get ready for dinner. His wife has already prepared dinner and all he has to do is serve it. Everything is so neatly laid out and he's wondering to himself how his wife was able to do this and be so organized. He is imagining that he doesn't think he'll be able to do this for two weeks. Later, the kids are sitting at the table with him.

One says, "The dinner tastes really good, Dad! I didn't know you could cook like this!"

Pastor Danig: "Well, I didn't cook the food—I simply served it."

"Oh," responds the older son. "Can you cook like Mom?"

Pastor Danig: "Well, I can cook some things and some of the food that I cook might taste a little different than Mom's cooking because we season things differently. I think our cooking styles differ but I can cook some things that taste really good. You know, kids, I don't know if I'll be cooking every night. I will probably have the babysitter do that some times and we'll eat out or have pizza night. Does that sound like fun or what?"

The kids celebrate by saying, "Yeaaaaahhh. Dad, can we go to McDonald's tomorrow?"

Pastor Danig: "I didn't have McDonald's planned for tomorrow but we'll see. Now guys, listen to me! Since your mother is out of town, you guys are going to help out around the house more than you normally do."

Kids: "Okay, Dad!"

Scene: Pastor Danig is at home resting on the couch and watching CNN. The kids are in the backroom playing Sony PlayStation.

As he's watching the news he's nearly falling asleep on the couch and the phone rings. His wife is on the other line and telling him that the plane arrived. He then falls asleep on the couch and at 3:37 in the morning he receives a phone call from Julya.

Julya speaks with a frantic voice: "Pastor Danig, I'm sorry to bother you but my baby's daddy is parked outside the apartment."

Pastor Danig: "Did you call the police?"

Julya: "No, I didn't call the police because he hasn't come to the door yet."

Pastor Danig: "How did you notice he was there?"

Julya: "I'm a night person and sometimes I get up. It was scary to me to see his car out there."

Pastor Danig: "Do you think he's dangerous and will he try to force his way in?"

Julya: "I see his car out there but I can't tell if he's in it or not!"

Pastor Danig. "Just make sure everything is locked and you need to call the cops to have them take a look. If he doesn't live there, then you need to have someone come in there and investigate the parking area. Call the security at your rental company and have them check the parking structure. They usually have an emergency number for things like this and I know that these complexes have some type of security."

Julya: "I'm really nervous…."

Pastor Danig: "Look, just call security and the police and go get some sleep. It isn't your job to worry now. Just stay in your home and wait for them to do their job. Call me when you're done just to let me know that you contacted the cops or security. I think I'll sleep better."

Julya: "Okay."

She calls security and they find out that the car that she reported was a car that belonged to a tenant. She then calls Pastor Danig and apologizes for the mistake.

Julya: "I think I'm stressing about my baby's daddy and I'm sorry for bothering you at such a crazy hour."

Pastor Danig: "Don't worry about it. It is part of my job as pastor and you wouldn't believe the amount of calls I used to get in the crazy hours of the morning. But, I'd like to say this before I get off the phone, you should consider getting some counseling over your baby's daddy situation. I'm not going to really push the issue but if you feel he's a danger you need to try to put yourself in a place of safety for you and your children. On that note, get some sleep and we'll see you today at work."

Scene: Pastor is at home trying to get breakfast together for his children, who are home for summer vacation:

He makes a phone call to the parks and recreation and schedules them for swimming lessons, which are scheduled to start next week. He then starts scrambling some eggs and putting bread in the toaster. He then walks over to the children's room and tells them, "Rise and shine. Get up and brush your teeth and wash your faces."

They reluctantly get up.

Child 1: "Dad, I'm tired and it is summer! Do we have to get up so early?"

Pastor Danig: "Yes, you do because it isn't summer break for me and I have to get you ready before I go to work. The babysitter will watch you guys for a few hours and I'll be home to take you to McDonald's for dinner. Now remember what I said, any bad news from the babysitter and you guys won't get to do any fun stuff that I have planned while your mom is away!"

The kids hurriedly get up and make their way to the bathroom.

Pastor Danig: "Okay, I want these rooms cleaned up and all of your dirty clothes in the hamper. Breakfast will be ready in 15 minutes so have those things done before you guys come to the table."

Pastor Danig goes back to the kitchen only to find that the toast is burnt. In his frustration, he tried to scrape the burn toast but it is too badly burnt. He then throws away the toast and then looks at the clock and it is 15 minutes before it is time for him to leave. The doorbell rings and the babysitter is standing at the door.

He quickly opens the door and says, "Hello, and you're just in time to help in the kitchen because I'm running late. I need to leave shortly and I want the kids to start eating before I leave, so can you serve them up so I can finished getting things together before I leave."

Babysitter: "Okay, Pastor, don't worry; I'll take care of it."

Pastor Danig: "Thanks!" He runs to the back room to get his things.

The kids run out and sit at the table and the babysitter brings the plates of food.

Babysitter: "What would you guys like to drink?"

Child 1: "I would like some orange juice!"

"I'll take some soda," said the other.

Babysitter: "Soda? Yeah, right, you're not drinking soda for breakfast!"

Child 2: "Our parents let us have soda with our breakfast! They said we can drink it so that we won't crave it when we get older!"

Babysitter: "Are you making this up?"

Child 1: "No, you can ask Dad!"

Babysitter: "I'm going to ask him and don't try to use psychology on me and think that I won't!"

Child 2: "Why do you need to confirm that with our dad? That's not what makes a good babysitter—always asking questions! He wouldn't be asking you to babysit if he didn't think you were mature enough to make decisions on this stuff."

Babysitter: "Okay, you're right, little child! Here's some milk and if you have a problem with it, YOU can take it up with your dad!"

Child 1 looks at Child 2 and says, "I can see this babysitter is going to be a problem!"

Babysitter: "That's why you guys need a babysitter. Drinking soda for breakfast is just a small example of how you're unable to watch yourselves! So since we're talking about sitting, how about sitting down and getting some breakfast and stop with all of the demands!"

Pastor Danig walks in the room and says to the children, "Okay, remember what I said, children, and when I return around 1 o'clock, I expect to hear good news from the babysitter!"

Child 1: "Bye, Dad!"

Scene: Returns home from work and the house is in disarray:

Pastor Danig: "What's going on?"

Babysitter: "I didn't think you'd be home this soon and we were going to clean up."

Pastor Danig: "You know I don't like what I see and you guys can forget about going out tonight. I want this house cleaned up! Go to your room now!"

The children slowly walk to their rooms.

Pastor Danig: "Okay, what happened? I thought you were here to keep things in order?"

Babysitter: "Well, things weren't so bad and we planned on cleaning up before you made it back home!" The babysitter says with a sarcastic voice, "We can still clean up!"

Pastor Danig's phone rings. As he's answering he says to the babysitter, "Okay, you guys go ahead and do that. I'll be in my study." He rushes to his study and shuts the door so that his wife will not hear the commotion in the background.

Maylee: "So how are things going?"

Pastor Danig: "Things are fine," he says with enthusiasm. "I just walked in and the babysitter is just about to leave. I need to talk to her so can I call you back?"

Maylee: "Sure, and I want to talk to the kids when you call me."

Pastor Danig: "Sure, honey, I'll do that! Anyway, how's your trip and how is your mother?"

Maylee: "She's doing fine. We're all down here helping out and it's really good to see family. I have some crazy family members out here. It seems that I'm the mediator and always squashing arguments that would otherwise get out of control. I think they like to argue and watch me break it up! Family is so crazy and fun and the same time. I really think I need to be closer to family and since we've moved away, I seem so disconnected from them. I'm still grateful that I get a chance to visit on a regular basis, though."

Pastor Danig: "Okay, I'll call you back, hun." Pastor Danig ends the call.

Scene: It's morning and Pastor Danig decides to stay home from the office:

He decides to take the rest of the week off so that he can focus on homemaking.

Pastor Danig: "Hello, this is Pastor Danig and I'm calling to let you know that I won't need you until next week. Actually don't worry about coming in today or tomorrow! In fact, I'll pay you for today since I've told you at the last minute."

Babysitter: "Is something wrong?"

Pastor Danig: "No, I have time off this week and just don't need a sitter right now! I'll call you next week, will you be available?"

Babysitter: "Sure, I'll be there."

Danig gets the boys ready as he's going to take them to the park with their bicycles.

Scene: Maylee at home with her family:

Maylee is sitting in the living room area with her family and relatives and the conversation is rather interesting and funny at times. Her family members called her Sewell when she was a child. Cousin Bell (47-year-old lady with a strong southern accent). Uncle Joe: (48-year-old uncle who's loud and obnoxious). The mother and father are also sitting in the living room.

Uncle Joe: "So what's it like being married to a pastor? Y'all don't get into anything freaky, huh? I mean, does the man quote scriptures in the bedroom?"

Everyone starts laughing.

"Sewell: "Actually our life isn't boring. In fact, it is far from boring and I think you have to be really strong to be the wife of a pastor because the job is ministry and the ministry affects what happens in our home. It's not easy because I have to share my husband with others."

Uncle Joe is holding a beer in his hand and his cigarette is burning in an ashtray on the coffee table next to him. "Oh, you mean to tell me that pastors are into group sex?"

Sewell: "I'm not talking about sharing like that. I mean when someone has a problem, he has to run to their aid as a pastor."

Uncle Joe sits there and takes a drag from the cigarette and ponders another smart comment. "Oh, that's nice! So he visits the sick and shut in?" He starts laughing hysterically.

Sewell: "No, no, no, you don't get it! Be quiet, Uncle Joe! I'm tired of your ignorant remarks."

Sewell is genuinely upset with Uncle Joe because he molested her when she was thirteen years old. No one knows about it and Sewell has anger inside of her because of it. Every time the family gets together he always comes around and comments about things she says. He hangs around so much to control conversations away from anyone who might try to talk about childhood experiences. He fears that one day she'll tell everyone about the event that changed her life forever. Uncle Joe's excessive drinking causes him to act indignant at times and Sewell seems to be the one who is able to settle him down when he gets out of control.

During their childhood years it seemed that everybody was involved in some type of sex act but everyone stayed quiet about it because it was taboo to talk about sex. Although it was wrong, it was a challenge to engage in something wrong at make sure no one ever found out. Everyone was sneaking around having sex in the hot sticky summers in the South. The preteen boys had a pact for the young girls and that was to make sure to not have sex if she started her period and if it was a cousin to have anal sex with her. During the hot summers when everyone was out of school on summer break, girls walked about with shorts to stay cool or were in swimsuits hanging out at the lake. Everyone would hang out at the lake and plan who they would get with and it didn't matter if it was a relative. The idea was to have sex because it was bragging rights for the boys.

Cousin Bell begins to comment on Sewell being married to a pastor. As she speaks of the strength of a pastor's wife and how they must sacrifice and be unselfish, Sewell goes back to the day in her mind when the molestation took place. It was a torrential, rainy afternoon and Sewell was in her room with her brother and sister. Uncle Joe was about 8 years older at the time. He was 21 years old and had been trying to get at Sewell since the previous summer. The other cousins were playing Atari and their minds were so immersed into the video games that t nothing around them seemed to matter. They couldn't care less about what their other sisters and brothers could have been doing in the room because their minds were focused on getting the highest score.

Scene: Twenty-seven years earlier: Children are in the basement taking turns playing the Atari video games:

While two boys are playing at a time, the others are watching. Some of the girls are running up and down the stairs, either going outside or hanging out in the cool basement.

Uncle Joe: "So Sewell, do you have a boyfriend?"

Sewell: "My parents don't allow us to have boyfriends."

Uncle Joe: "Are you kidding?"

Sewell: "No, you know that kids still sneak around and have a boyfriend even though their parents tell them that they aren't allowed."

Uncle Joe: "Have you ever had sex?"

Sewell: "No, I haven't had sex! I'm only 13 and my parents told me to wait until I'm married!"

Uncle Joe: "Well, you're one of the few. I know most girls in this town have had sex and it's fun! You know you'll hear the stories of girls getting pregnant and their parents sending them away so no one will know about it. They do this because it's obvious that they couldn't control every second of their kids' life. They don't want their kids doing this stuff because they know it's fun and parents don't want their kids having too much fun. Do you know that sex feels really good?"

Sewell: "Well, I never had sex so I don't know that it feels really good. Some of my friends told me that they didn't like it and just did it so they can have a boyfriend."

Uncle Joe: "Well, you should try it sometime and you should do it with someone you trust."

Sewell: "I'm not doing that until I get married! I don't know what to do with sex and I don't want to be like some of those girls out there who are getting pregnant and getting in trouble."

Uncle Joe: "That's what I mean. You should do it with someone you trust because we all can keep it a secret and no one will ever know. And on top of that, you'll have fun doing it. I know how to do it so that you won't get pregnant."

Sewell: "You're my uncle! I'm not going to have sex with my uncle!"

It was becoming more evident that she was yielding because her initial response was that she would not have sex until she was married. Uncle Joe realized her vulnerability and wanted to begin the grooming process with the mindset that she would eventually give in.

Uncle Joe: "That's why it's a good thing! We can keep it a secret and no one will ever know. Family sticks together and we have this honor that family won't rat each other out. So you should let me teach you how to do it because if you get a boyfriend later, you're not going to know what to do and he can get you pregnant! You can have fun doing it with me and no one will ever have to know!"

Sewell: "I thought having sex with family members is incest. Isn't that incest?" Sewell begins to say it in a firm voice. "You're not supposed to have sex with family members!"

Uncle Joe: "I'm like a distant family member and it is incest if you do it with your brothers and sisters! I just want to show you some things so that you won't make mistakes later! Your parents aren't going to tell you about this stuff and you're going to get messed up when you get with some guy that doesn't know what he's doing! We aren't going to go all the way!" Uncle Joe quickly changes the subject. "Hey, when the rain slows down, let's go for a ride in my dad's truck to the market and get some pork rinds and candy!"

Sewell: "No, I'll wait for you to come back."

Uncle Joe: "No, I want you to come with me! We'll only be gone for a few minutes—it's just down the street! Come on, you'll be glad that you did and you can get your favorite candy!"

Sewell: "Okay, let me get my jacket."

While she runs upstairs to grab her purple jean jacket, he gets into the truck and starts it up. She then dashes out of the house, runs to the passenger side of the 1957 Chevy pickup and struggles to open the door. He slowly backs the truck out of the dirt worn by tires and grass driveway and pulls out onto the two-lane street leading to the Piggly Wiggly market, which is about five miles up the street. As they are driving, Uncle Joe starts the conversation on sex again.

Scene at the grandparents' house:

Later that evening the other kids fell asleep on the floor and the video game was in pause mode on the TV screen. It was 2:20 in the morning and Uncle Joe and Sewell were still awake.

Uncle Joe: "Hey, let's play Space Invaders and see who gets the highest score. The winner of each game gets to ask the person to do something and you have to do what the person asks you to do no matter what!"

Sewell: "That isn't fair because I'm not that good at this game!"

Uncle Joe: "Well, I'm not that good at this game either and you'll probably end up beating me!"

Sewell thought to herself that this would be fun since she is pretty good at the game but in comparison to her brothers, she's not that good. So they played the first game of Space Invaders, which took about 20 minutes before it was realized that Sewell had the higher score.

She won the first game and then Uncle Joe said, "Well, I lost fairly so you get to tell me to do something and you can think of anything and I'll have to do it. Now don't make me do anything that will cause me to kill myself!"

Sewell laughs and then said, "Okay, you can go upstairs and get one of those jars of pig's feet and eat all the feet in the bottle!"

Uncle Joe loved pig's feet and he thought to himself that this was going to be easy. He quietly ran upstairs so as to not wake up his grandparents, who were asleep in the other rooms. He never understood why his grandparents slept in separate rooms.

As he made it downstairs with the bottle of pig's feet, he pretended that it was the most disgusting thing to do and begged her to not make him eat all of the pig's feet in the jar.

Sewell: "Didn't you say that the person has to do what they say no matter what?"

Uncle Joe: "You're right but this is really disgusting!"

He then opened the jar and pulled out all three dripping with vinegar pig's feet and placed them on a plate. He then started to eat them and closed his eyes in disgust but in reality he was enjoying every slithery removal of the pig's flesh off of the bones of the feet. Sewell turned her head and laughed in disgust as he worked on each pig's foot. When he completed the third pig's foot, he sat there for a moment and said, "I feel like I'm going to throw up!"

Sewell said, "You better get out of here and go to the bathroom, I'm not trying to get sprayed with no pig's feet!"

Uncle Joe sat there for a few minutes and then said, "What made you ask me to do this?"

Sewell: "Well, I don't know how people eat pig's feet and I got tired of seeing it in Grandma's cabinets, so I thought you'd be the person to get it out of my sight!"

Uncle Joe: "Well, I have to do my best to try to beat you at the next game!"

Sewell thought to herself that this would be another easy win for her because she beat him badly in the last game. They played at least five more games until Uncle Joe finally won one game. It was his turn to get Sewell to do something. She told him to go easy on her because her last four challenges to him were easy.

Uncle Joe: "Okay, this one is going to be really easy!" He whispers so he doesn't wake anyone with what he's about to say. "Take off your shorts and panties and let me look at your thing for 60 seconds."

Sewell: "Huh? Are you crazy, I'm not showing you that! That is embarrassing!"

Uncle Joe: "Don't worry, we're family and no one is going to say anything! Remember what we said, that you have to do what the other person says, no matter what!"

Sewell thought to herself that he did everything she asked him to do without question and this was only 60 seconds of a non-life-threatening event. She really didn't want him to see her private area. She pulled the blanket from the side and covered herself and then lowered her pants and panties to her knees.

Uncle Joe: "Well, you're going to have to remove the blanket because I can't see it."

Sewell hurriedly slid the blanket out of the way say that the dimly lit light shone on her and then he stared at it for 15 seconds before she rushed to pull up her shorts.

Uncle Joe: "That wasn't sixty seconds!"

Sewell: "It was sixty seconds, your clock is slow!"

Uncle Joe: "It looks pretty."

Sewell: "It's just a bit of hair between the legs! Let's do something that does not involve having to remove clothes!"

Uncle Joe: "We were just having fun and no one has to know what we did—it's just between us!"

Sewell: "I wouldn't dare tell anyone that I showed you my thing!"

Uncle Joe: "Don't worry, it's our little secret! Have you ever seen a guy's thing?"

"Yes, I've seen my brother's thing and the boy I kissed in middle school showed me his thing. I'm not going to let you show me your thing and I'm not going to show you my thing again! Somebody might walk in or my brother or sister might wake up!"

Uncle Joe: "I'll show you under the blanket like you did and if anyone walks in, we can just act like we're asleep like everyone else. It won't take long!" He unzips his pants and pulls it down slightly and pulls out his erect penis.

She jumps and says, "Why is it hard and long like that?"

Uncle Joe: "It got that way when I looked at your private!"

He then pulls up his pants and Sewell says, "I don't want to see anymore."

Uncle Joe: "You're going to see it again one day! Some guy is going to be your boyfriend and you guys are going to have sex! That's what boyfriends and girlfriends do! They have sex!"

Sewell: "You don't have to have sex to have a boyfriend!"

Uncle Joe: "That's all you can do and it's a lot of fun and it feels good!"

Sewell: "That's all you can think of because that's all you talk about!"

Uncle Joe: "Hey, let me show you something! Let's go in the room next to the bathroom."

Sewell: "Why?"

Uncle Joe: "I just want to show you something!"

They walk over to the other room, which is next to the bathroom.

He then says, "Let's go in here, where there is better lighting. You can see better and no one will walk in on us. We just have to be really quiet! Come on, it's no big deal!"

So they tiptoe into the bathroom and close and lock the door. Uncle Joe drops his pants and then pulls Sewell's pants down. He then tells her to turn around and then he quickly puts his penis between her buttocks and gently slides it up and down.

Sewell: "What are you doing?"

Uncle Joe: "I'm showing you how good this is going to feel!"

Sewell: "Well, hurry up and show me what you're talking about because I don't want to get caught in the bathroom with you!"

He puts more oil between her legs and he begins penetrating.

She makes a sound and says, "Hold on, that doesn't feel right!"

Uncle Joe: "That's how it is in the beginning!"

Scene: Twenty-seven years back to the present day in the living room:

Cousin Bell: "Sewell, where is your mind? You seem to be off in daydreamers' land!"

Sewell: "No, I'm just a little tired—probably a little jetlag."

Meanwhile, her presence at her grandmother's house brings back memories of her childhood that she does not wish to discuss.

Mother: "Well, sweetie, you should go on in the room and get some rest."

Sewell: "I think I'll do that in a minute."

Sewell's dad: "I would still like to know more about how you're doing being a pastor's wife."

Sewell: "I don't want to talk about it now, Dad, please! Maybe we can talk about it tomorrow when I have a little more energy. Right now I'm a good listener and I'm enjoying listening to all of you talk."

Uncle Joe: "Okay, ain't nobody that tired from flying. You weren't flying! You were sitting in the plane and the machines did all of the work and the pilots were handling the controls! So the pilots should be tired and they aren't here, so you need to talk if we ask you a question."

Sewell: "Shut up, Uncle Joe!"

The children start asking all sorts of questions during the movie and Danig gets a bit frustrated because he wants to enjoy the movie.

Pastor Danig: "Hey, guys, I just want to enjoy the movie! Can you minimize all of the questions?"

Child 1: "Dad, if I don't ask questions now, I'm not going to know what's going on and it will be too late if we ask you later!"

Pastor Danig: "Okay, but you're asking too many questions and too frequently! We can't hear what they're saying in the movie if you're asking me questions while they're problem explaining what's going on! So ask questions later!"

Child 1: "Dad, when is Mom coming home?"

Pastor Danig: "She's going to be in Louisiana for two weeks. She won't be back until the end of next week."

Child 2: "I miss Mom! Can I talk to her on the phone?"

Pastor Danig: "We'll call them tomorrow because they're three hours ahead and I'm sure they're asleep by now! Let's just enjoy the rest of the movie, guys."

As they are continuing the movie Pastor Danig's cellphone rings and Julya is on the line. He presses the ignore button because he is adamant about enjoying the rest of the movie without any interruptions. Five minutes pass and the phone rings again. It's Julya again and Pastor Danig decides to answer.

Pastor Danig: "Hello, what's going on?"

Julya: "I need to talk to you about my baby's daddy again. He keeps showing up at these unexpected places and I don't want my children around this type of drama. He drinks or smokes weed and when he is high like that, he doesn't think straight. When that stuff wears off he, seems like there's a possibility for him getting his life together. I don't want to call the cops because there are so many of us in the penal system. I don't want my children to be mad at me when they find out that I was the one who helped put their father in jail. I really believe God that he will change one day and I don't love him enough to be married to him. It's not like he wants to get married anyway because he's just in it for the sex! I don't want to see him messed up for the sake of the children. He came by earlier and I didn't answer the door and I think he's going to come back. Pastor, I'm really afraid and I really don't want to stay here."

Pastor Danig: "Do you have any relatives that you can stay with until you figure out what to do?"

"I can probably stay with my mother but I don't want to bug her this late with the children."

Pastor Danig: "I think you should just stay positioned in your home and don't answer the door until tomorrow. I know it sounds like you're imprisoning yourself but do this until tomorrow and I make sure you take some steps to get immediate help tomorrow. You don't have to live your life like this and it sounds like you want the best for him but if you feel that you and your children are in some sort of danger then you need to do what needs to be done."

Julya: "I don't want him in jail because that's where he's going if I call the authorities."

Pastor Danig: "Okay, I'm trying to hear you but this man does drugs and is a danger to you and your children. Now are you going to wait for something tragic to happen before the authorities are called? He's obviously continuing with drug use and it's only going to get worse. Don't fool yourself about wanting the best for someone who is using a substance that makes his reality distorted. He could harm or even kill you under the influence of the drugs and not realize what he's doing! So, unless he's in a drug treatment program, you cannot hope for the best for him and keep him out of the system that you fear. It might be for his own good if he doesn't voluntarily get help. I want you to promise me that you'll do something about this tomorrow."

Julya: "Okay."

Pastor Danig says a prayer before hanging up the phone: "Lord God, help Julya make the right decision that's best for herself, her children and even the father of her children. We ask for your protection over her home as she sleeps tonight and Lord, if it's in your will, deliver the father of her children from the wrongful lifestyle that he's involved in."

Julya: "Thank you so much for praying for me and I think I'll sleep better tonight knowing what I must do tomorrow."

Pastor Danig: "Good, I'm glad to hear that you will be doing something about it tomorrow. I will talk to you later."

Julya: "Goodnight."

He is stressed out and wishing that he didn't tell the babysitter to take off. He calls the babysitter to see if she's available but it goes to her voicemail. In his desperation for help, he thinks of who can possibly come over to help without alerting his wife that he needs help while she's away. He gets his phone and looks through his contacts to see if he could get someone to come over and watch the kids while he leaves to work on some church stuff. He's exhausted and tells the children to go to their room.

Pastor Danig: "Okay, guys, I want you guys to clean up the room and when you're done, let me know so I can check it. If it doesn't meet my approval, you guys are going to be in a lot of trouble. I only want to check one time and if it isn't to my satisfaction you're going to do more chores than you've ever imagined."

He goes to the den area and sits down to try and get some work done at home. He begins checking and responding to work email. While checking email, his phone is ringing off the hook. People from the church are calling him and he's spending time on the phone answering phones and ministering to people with their problems. It's as though he's at work because he's scheduling a telephone conference in an hour. He leaves the den area and confronts his children.

Pastor Danig: "Okay, kids, how's it coming with the cleaning? I'm ready to check the rooms and I need you guys to be finished in the next fifteen minutes because I'm going to need an hour of quiet while I do this conference call at work. When I'm in the conference call, you guys can play PlayStation, watch TV, or read a book. I expect it to be quiet and no foolishness because I'm going to be doing business. Did I make myself clear?"

The children said "Yes" in unison.

Scene: In the den and on the conference call with the staff at the church:

Chairperson of meeting: "Okay, we have everyone dialed in via Skype. We have a quorum and can commence the meeting on this day, June 17th at 10 A.M." The chairperson of the meeting brought up the agenda items from the last meeting and made a motion to approve the minutes to the last meeting. Chairperson: "All in favor say I. The new agenda items listed the amount of money that was raised from the convention and expenditures. One of the items on the list was for the August conference, which was another four-day conference."

As they began discussing scheduling and accommodations, the children could be heard in the background fighting and screaming.

Pastor Danig: "Please excuse me." He clicked the mute button on his laptop and rushed to see what was going on with the children. Pastor Danig: "I told you guys to play quietly while I handle my work and the moment I'm not watching, you guys decide to fight. Now I'm separating you."

The kids started crying and blaming each other for what was happening and Pastor Danig heard nothing but crying and screaming. He grabbed the eldest son and told the other to get in his bed and wait until he was done with the meeting.

Pastor Danig: "I better not hear one word out of you. You have already ruined my meeting and I'm missing important work-related business because you guys don't know how to listen! I want you to know that when this meeting is over, I'm tearing up somebody's bottom!"

Child 1: "Dad, can you tear up the bottom now 'cause I don't want to think about it!"

Pastor Danig: "No, and I might change my mind if you guys behave!"

He rushes back to the den and un-mutes the computer. The meeting continues for another 20 minutes and then his phone rings. Julya is on the line and then for a moment in all of the frustration, he mutes the computer and picks up the phone.

Julya: "I need to talk to you as soon as possible!"

Pastor Danig: "I'm in the meeting, which is about over, so let me call you back in about ten minutes."

Julya: "It cannot wait, can you please talk to me now!"

Pastor Danig: "Please—very quickly because I need to finish this meeting."

Julya: "I don't want to stay at my place tonight because I went to the precinct today to file a restraining order and one of my baby's daddy's friends told him that I was down there filing the report."

Pastor Danig: "How did they know you were filing a police report?"

Julya: "Because they were there and they overheard the conversation that I had with the officer behind the desk. It seems like he has friends all over the place and I feel like he's got people watching me! I don't want to go stay with my mother because she has enough of her own problems."

Pastor Danig: "Okay, look, I don't want to sound as if I don't care but I really must end this meeting because I'm actually involved in the meeting from my home on the internet meeting and they're about to end. I need to call you back."

Julya: "Can you just put me on hold because I don't feel safe around here."

Pastor Danig: "Okay, let me make an offer or should I say...," *briefly pauses*, "suggestion. I need help over here with my children while my wife is out for another week. I really cannot handle this by myself and my babysitter is no longer available. I realize you work at the church, so you can work from home and still get paid and I'll pay you extra to help with the children. There's a computer in the guestroom that you can work from when you're not helping with the kids. You can bring your kids over and help me with my kids while I handle church stuff. I'll just introduce you to the children as the babysitter. You can spend the night in the extra room. You can bring your children over tonight or tomorrow if you can and we can discuss the details. As for now, let me finish up this meeting and I'll see you later."

Julya: "Thank you, Pastor, and I think this will give me an opportunity to sort things out since I'll be away from that drama for a couple of days."

Pastor Danig: "I'll text you the address and directions to my house."

Scene: Maylee is on the phone with her husband:

Maylee: "So how are things going with the children and how's the babysitter doing?"

Pastor Danig: "The babysitter worked the first couple of days and I decided to work from home yesterday and today. I'll be calling in another babysitter since the babysitter we've used seemed to let the children run amuck. The house was in disarray when I came home one day and I was only gone for half the day. Anyway, no big deal, I'll just get someone else if needed."

Maylee: "So you're managing okay with the kids and work?"

Pastor Danig: "Yeah, things are good and I have some flexibility with work but sometimes I have to go in because you certainly can't teleconference everything!"

Maylee: "Well, I'm about ready to come home because my family is stressing me out a little. My mother is doing okay but there are enough family members here to help out. I feel so distant from family because we're so far away and maybe I overexaggerated her need for all of this help. We need to be closer to family because that's what's important. I feel like I'm missing out."

Pastor Danig: "You just said that they're getting on your nerves and now you feel like you're missing something. Maybe the distance thing is a good thing and visiting gives you a chance to catch up."

Maylee: "Well, maybe they wouldn't be getting on my nerves if we were closer to home. I think they're so happy when I arrive and then as the days go on, everyone starts acting silly. If we were closer, I would not have to stay for days at a time and when things got out of control, I could just leave and see them next weekend, for instance."

Pastor Danig: "Well, we are your immediate family and we can work out you having to see them more frequently if that's a problem."

Maylee: "Okay, well, I'm going to get off this phone for now. Call me if things get too much out of control!"

Pastor Danig: "Don't worry. Things are okay on this end."

Scene: Next morning: Julya shows up with her children and Danig lets her in and shows her around the house and the room that she will be staying in for the week:

She thanks him for allowing her and her children to stay while working to watch his children.

Pastor Danig: "Okay, well, you're an hour early!"

Julya: "Yeah, I thought I'd come early being that I'm bringing my children. I thought that you probably needed time to show me what you needed me to do."

Pastor Danig: "Yeah, it's no problem and here's the room you'll be staying in."

They walk to the kitchen.

Pastor Danig: "You don't have to cook anything! The kids love cereal and you'll find that in this cabinet. And don't worry about waking them up at a certain time. You can let them sleep in—they'll probably sleep until 11 or 12. It's easier that way and you can actually do your work on your administrative assistant tasks from this computer while your children are asleep. This computer networks to the church database, so it's like being at the church. You will be able to get your work done here just as easily as you would if you were there! Please relax in your room and make yourself at home! There's enough room for you and the boys in this room."

Julya: "Okay, I'll get things in order and let the boys crash because they were up throughout the night with all of the baby daddy's drama."

Pastor Danig: "You do that!" as he looks her in admiration.

Pastor Danig thinks to himself, "I can't believe I have this woman in my house and the thoughts that are going through my mind. She is beautiful. Is my admiration of her wrong? Is her beauty enhanced by such a sweet attitude? My wife is beautiful but her attitude sucks. I'm confused and I know what I'm doing is an appearance of evil but I don't believe my intentions are evil. But they must be evil because I'm a married man and I have another woman in my home that I admire. She's not just a babysitter who's helping me out and perhaps I'm helping her out but there's more to it. I've now put myself in a tempting situation. I'm going to be strong and not say anything that might lead to something and she probably won't yield to my foolishness anyway, so I'm good—I think…. I feel like David. When I want to do right my flesh wants to do the wrong thing. I know what is right and yet I find myself in this situation. Am I wrong for feeling this way? Is my wife pushing me away with her complaining and inattentiveness to my needs? I feel this woman whom I don't know that well is captivating my thoughts. She's strong and resilient and I'm amazed how she's dealing with a shiftless person in her life—how she's trying to look at the good in all of the bad that this person represents."

He subdues his thoughts and moves on to the real agenda and that was for her to watch the children. While he is getting ready to leave, he thinks that he must figure out a way to un-invite Julya and help her in another way. He is feeling guilty because her presence has overwhelmed his thoughts and in his weakness, he decides to tell her that he will accept this arrangement tonight but will help her with other arrangements while she works on the baby's daddy drama.

Pastor Danig: "Julya, I'm leaving—I'll be in the office for a couple of hours. When I get back, I want to sit down and talk to you about this arrangement."

Julya: "Okay, Pastor Danig."

Pastor Danig: "I'll probably get home before the children awaken, so things should be easy for you."

Julya: "I'll see you when you get back and thank you again."

Scene: Pastor Danig at the church office:

Deacon: "Pastor, can we talk for a minute?"

Danig: "Sure, what is it?"

Deacon: "I'll wait 'til you're available."

Pastor Danig: "Give me a few minutes."

Deacon: "Sure, it will be brief."

Pastor Danig walks in the conference room and the deacon looks concerned.

Pastor Danig: "What's on your mind, Deacon?"

Deacon: "Close the door, please."

Danig closes the door and takes a seat in on the seat at the head of the table.

Deacon: "So, Pastor, what's going on with Julya? She seems to be having some problems at the home-front and she's not in today? I was told that she didn't call to let anyone know that she wouldn't be in today. Did you hear anything?"

Pastor Danig: "It's fine, Deacon. Don't worry about Julya, it's taken care of and she's helping me with things and yes, I understand that she's having problems at the home-front and I'm also helping her with this."

Deacon: "Okay, let's talk man to man and off the books for a minute. Do you have an attraction for Julya?"

Pastor Danig: "She's a pretty lady and my attraction to her is one of admiration. She has a pleasant attitude despite all of the things she's going through. I am a married man and if your concerns are that I might involve myself with her, then you're wrong."

Deacon: "I didn't ask you whether you were married! That much is understood! There are a lot of married men that get caught up in this sort of thing, so don't act like you don't know what I'm talking about. I've seen your interaction with her and it seems a bit more than just a worker-to-supervisor experience."

Pastor Danig: "Well, we have to work closely as she is my administrative assistant. I don't know what more I can say. She works as my assistant. She happens to be a lady and she is attractive and so naturally, people are going to make assumptions. Perhaps you're the one with the problem."

Deacon: "I don't think so. I think you know what I'm talking about and as the deacon, I'm going to ask you to be careful. Again I've seen this sort of thing with pastors and she does good work and happens to be attractive."

Danig: "Don't you worry, Deacon—I think I'm able to handle myself and won't compromise my position here as pastor."

Deacon; "So is that where your concern is mostly? If that is the case, then perhaps I'll need to help you. Your intentions might be sincere and if you put yourself in a position where you are tempted."

Pastor Danig interrupts, "Deacon, that will be all! There's no need to further discuss this and thank you for your concern!"

Danig hurriedly leaves the office and grabs his briefcase and heads out the door. Danig arrives at home and to his surprise, his children and her children are still asleep and Julya is sitting on the couch.

He said, "I decided to come home early and things at the office seem to be okay."

Julya gets up and walks toward Danig in an alluring and seductive posture. "I never told you thank you for what you've done. I feel safe over here and things back at the apartment are so ghetto, dangerous, and loud! I really need to move and get my kids out of that hostile environment."

Pastor Danig: "Well, I understand! I grew up in an environment where it seemed like your life was on the line on every front. I'm amazed that I'm still alive after being in such a dangerous place for so many years. I guess when you're young, you don't pay much attention to the danger that exists and the older you get, you appreciate the delicacy of life and you live each day like it is very precious. I mean you value every moment and you don't want to miss the opportunity to enjoy the life that God has given you."

Julya: "Wow, you say that with such compassion. Since you're saying all of this, I must say that since every moment is special and you don't want to miss the opportunity to enjoy life, I now feel the courage to say this."

Pastor Danig raises his eyebrow.

Julya: "I wanted to tell you this and I've been too embarrassed because I thought you might think that I was weird or ungodly. The truth of the matter is that I am attracted to a married man! It's strange because I'm not the home wrecker. I witnessed that type of woman literally destroy the home I grew up in. I don't know why I'm telling you all of this but my father let another woman come into our household and basically break up the beautiful family I thought we had when we were growing up. Never in a million years did I ever dream of my dad running off with another woman but it happened. Yes, it happened in the household I grew up in—not the other person as we are so used to seeing it happen to. I grew up with anger in my heart because the secure feeling that I had growing up and knowing that Mom and Dad were there was no longer the case anymore. My parents split up and my mom was left home to try to raise us by herself. I was angry and my anger was toward my dad and the other woman. I must say that most of my anger was toward my dad because he let it happen."

Pastor Danig: "I'm sorry to hear that and it is nice to know that you're not the home-wrecking type. I think it is okay to be attracted to someone if you admire the person that they are. You have to also realize that such an attraction does not mean that you have to act on your attraction nor does it mean that you are supposed to be with that person. Many people have attractions for the wrong reasons and then they want to be with a person who is already married. I've always been amazed at the challenge of married couples and how people seem to be attracted to those who are already married. There are so many people in this world who'd like to be with someone but because they're stuck in this little world of thinking that there is no one else. We become impulsive and run after someone who looks good, has a decent job, and seemingly has a nice personality. We look at our situation, which seems to be dismal, and then we act on emotions and desperation. We convince ourselves that we are better than the other person that we try to compete with in so many ways and we know that we can have what that person seems to have. We are deceived and then we act on such sentiments. The men who are the recipients of such an attraction find it appealing and feel that such woman is giving him some type of attention that he might not be getting at home. In fact, most men are not strong enough to deal with these attractions and they let those women come into their lives. They are weak minded and are not strong in the word. I don't mean to be harsh but I've seen people get caught up in such scandal. The men, that is—they get caught up and respond by fulfilling their lustful desires. They get so caught up to the point of not caring how they impact others' lives. I mean, it isn't just the spouse who is adversely affected but if children are involved, they get emotionally messed up in the whole process, which usually has lifelong impacts. You can attest to this in your testimony about your parents' marriage. The parents don't think about this and they rush off fulfilling their desires while forgetting about their loved ones. Now the selfish picture in all of this is that we think that if it is done secretly and with minimal drama, the children will not be affected. The truth of the matter is that most children will be affected even if they don't see it coming. They are upset and when they get older will wonder why Mom or Dad wasn't good enough for each other. They sometimes blame themselves and feel that if they weren't in the picture that maybe the parents would not have stayed together as long as they did or perhaps they might have stayed together if it weren't for them. There are so many mixed emotions and then the kids are so jacked up that they sometimes live a lifestyle that is similar to what they saw happen to their parents. For instance, if the child is in a bad relationship, they might think to themselves that they don't deserve to be in a good relationship because the parents had a bad one. It is the self-fulfilling prophesy as people will think that they can't do much better than what they've seen their parents go through or they will simply lower their standards because it seems like an easier route. I think it is sad and unless people break away from the curse of such a negative self-fulfilling prophesy, these conditions will remain in families from generations to generations."

Julya: "You've said some interesting things and I'm wondering if my feeling is because I witnessed my dad get snatched away by another woman. Was it her fault or his fault? I don't know who to blame for this. I find myself in situations like you've mentioned. My parents went in different directions and it could have happened with minimal drama but I find myself in a situation where I'm attracted to a married man. Yes, he's married but is he really supposed to be with the woman that he's married to? No one really knows. I don't know that my father is still married to this woman that in my mind feels that she stole him from my mom. Maybe it was intended for them to be together and my mom and I was a mistake."

Pastor Danig: "You and your mom are not mistakes and there are events in life that we cannot always explain! There are people that we get to know and who might do harm or good to us! They will impact our life in some way but we have to realize that all things work together for good to them that love the Lord and are called according to his purpose."

Julya: "Well, I love the Lord and what if I'm called according to his purpose? Then in my mind, it might be that the man that I'm attracted to could be my husband. He doesn't know it and neither do I. Would I be wrong to hold this inside of me or would it be in my best interest to let him know? Would I be stepping out of the will of God if I disobeyed and held my feeling inside of me? No one really knows! There are a lot of people getting married who really don't belong together. It might not be the will of God for them to be together and yet they enter into these major covenants only to find out that they were incompatible. Yes, I've seen so many of my friends get married for the wrong reasons. They run after some dude whom they think is attractive and they try to trap them with sex and even pregnancy. Yes, it's the oldest trick in the book but desperate women do these things when they panic and see their lives as insignificant. A woman starts to panic when she feels that her life isn't significant. It isn't just a career that makes a woman feel significant but it is someone loving her. She wants to be loved and nurtured and she wants that person who loves and nurtures her to share a child with her so that she can nurture the child. These are some things that make a woman feel significant because I know that when we were brought up as children, we always had the dollhouses while my brothers had the army toys, Tonkas, and model airplanes. We were taught as young as we can remember that our role as a woman one day must be the traditional role even though we've ventured off into doing career-oriented things outside of domestic work."

Pastor Danig: "You have pretty good insight and I'm amazed at what I'm hearing. I didn't know that your perspective on this was this profound. Anyway, I must say that you are right and everyone's experience is different, of course. Since you realize that you don't want to fall into the same desperation that you've seen your friends, perhaps your attraction to a married man will stop at the attraction."

Julya: "But I'm saying, I don't want it to stop there! That is why I'm saying something now. How do you know that the attraction that I'm having is wrong? It's only wrong based on what is present now. Yes, it is wrong when you look at it from the perspective of a man who's married but it might be right if his marriage is not ordained of God. He might be in something for a season and perhaps entered into the agreement for the wrong reason and outside of the will of God. No one will ever know unless something is said or done."

Pastor Danig: "Okay, now that sounds impulsive!"

Julya: "Perhaps impulsiveness is an order! Sitting by idle while people go on living their lives miserably might be worse than someone waking them up via impulsiveness. I know that the scripture says that open rebuke is better than secret love. I know I'm probably misinterpreting this scripture but what if it means in this case that my secret love for this person will never get noticed unless I openly say something. I think it is important to say something instead of going through life never knowing what the outcome of something is going to be."

Pastor Danig: "Some things are better left unsaid. You might be putting yourself in harm's way. You have to exercise a little caution and wisdom when it comes to things like this. Your impulse is wrong, I must say, because you might be potentially wrecking someone's marriage and home. You might be that homewrecker who took someone away from something beautiful and the weak-minded individual might have been allured to you via a sexual infatuation."

Julya: "It sounds like blame is being passed on the woman but I know it's not always the woman who's going after men."

Pastor Danig: "A man that findeth a wife findeth a good thing."

Julya: "The Bible tends to be sexist in that manner. The wife cannot be found if she's hiding or sitting back waiting for the man to come his way. I believe her role is important in positioning herself."

Pastor Danig: "Positioning?"

Julya: "Yes, positioning!"

Pastor Danig: "Hmmm, okay. Well, I appreciate your openness and for sharing this with me. I will keep what you say in the strictest of confidence."

Julya: "You sound robotic and I don't care about you keeping this in the strictest of confidence."

Pastor Danig: "No, I just wanted you to know that I'm not one of those pastors that runs around telling people's business."

Julya: "Well, I don't know how true that is, Pastor. Pastors tend to say stuff like that and then end up using it as part of their sermons. They think people are stupid because they try to change one or two things but the members know what you're talking about. If I was ashamed at what I needed to say or felt it needed to be kept in the strictest of confidence, I would not have opened my mouth."

Pastor Danig: "I see."

Julya: "What do you think I should do and please tell me without sounding robotic and throwing a million scriptures at me?"

Pastor Danig: "If the man is married, you need to steer clear. There are plenty of fish in the sea, as my parents would tell me when I thought some girl was the one for me. I was so caught up in the physical and maybe a lot of this was just infatuation. I believe you're infatuated and you really need to steer clear."

Julya: "I had a feeling you'd say something like this. I respect your opinion and I'm going to go with my heart."

Pastor Danig: "Okay, so who's this married man that you're having these feelings for?" "I don't think I should tell you that because that is proprietary information and you might say something."

Pastor Danig: "Excuse me. You've told me this much and now you want to play the proprietary information game."

Julya: "Well, yes, we should only know in part just like God has us. We know in part and the more information I give you, the easier it is for you to try to pass some type of judgment. I think it is safe to say that you know enough to pray for my condition and I hope that in your prayer, you'll take self out of it and let the Lord have his way."

Danig thinks to himself, "This woman is tripping but she seems to be on to something." He now wonders who this person might be and he's thinking that it might be him that she is talking about.

Pastor Danig: "I'm glad that we got a chance to talk about this and changing the subject to something that I wanted to talk about earlier. This temporary arrangement is dangerous! I mean you staying here while my wife is out of town. I can help you with another arrangement if you feel unsafe at your place. You can still watch the children during the day while I'm away at work."

Julya: "Does this have anything to do with what I told you?"

Pastor Danig: "Not at all—in fact, that's why I came home earlier today, so that I could discuss it with you and immediately help you with another arrangement. I was also in a meeting with one of the deacons and he indicated that he thought that our professional interaction looked a bit suspicious. I don't want people thinking that you're my mistress. Rumors tend to travel very quickly in this church world. It's like a soap opera and I don't want to give in to such foolishness."

Julya: "You agreed to let me come over here and stay the night because you cared. You didn't want to see me in danger and you listened. You heard my fears and you acted swiftly. I think that is a very caring thing and I am appreciative of that. Don't let these sterile, fake, hypocritical people that you work around try to turn your good works into evil. That deacon that you're talking about likes me because he's always staring at me and he's married."

Pastor Danig: "Excuse me, but I don't think you know who I'm talking about."

Julya: "I know who you're talking about. Only someone who's trying to get at me would be concerned about what you're doing. He's been watching our interaction very closely because I've seen him in the meetings and at the office. He looks at me like he wants to have sex. He gives me the creeps and his breath stinks. He talks too much and he doesn't drink enough water. He's got that cottonmouth thing going—just nasty! Don't you guys have seminars on some etiquette on public speakers? No person should stand in the pulpit and grab a microphone with nasty breath and cotton mouth! It distracts people and I don't know how anyone can sit up there and listen to this uncircumcised Philistine. He's a major hypocrite and you're listening to this guy or letting him influence you?"

Pastor Danig laughs hysterically and he tries to defend his stance but Julya continues.

"Most, if not all, of the people that you're working around are a bunch of hypocrites trying to act like they're saved." She exclaimed, "You can't be all super holy in this society that we live in! There are too many distractions, too many conveniences, and too many temptations."

Pastor Danig: "Would you consider yourself a distraction?"

Julya: "I don't know what you mean...."

Pastor Danig: "To me, that is."

Julya: "To you? So you consider me a distraction?"

Pastor Danig: "Well, no, but I think you can be because you're a beautiful lady."

Julya: "So you think I'm beautiful. Perhaps you're distracted by me."

Pastor Danig: "Okay, I don't want to be distracted and that's why I would like to tell you about your living arrangements. I have some friends who own an apartment complex in a nicer neighborhood and I can call them to see if they have any vacancies over there. The rent might be a lot more than what you're paying but I'll see if they have anything that might affordable."

Julya: "I have a section-8 certificate—do you know if they accept section 8?"

Pastor Danig: "I don't know but I'll ask them. Usually, in the nicer neighborhoods, they don't or they might have a small percentage of the units that they will allow section 8."

Julya: "I really appreciate that." Julya thinks, "This man is really looking out for me. He cares more than my baby's daddy!"

She stands close to Pastor Danig and he looks at her nervously as if she is too close. She is basically in proximity for a kiss and he looks at her and leans over and kisses her on the cheek. He pulls back and says, "I don't know why I did that and I feel that I've done something so wrong!"

Julya: "You're feeling guilty about something that you wanted to do! I don't think it is wrong and the kiss was on the cheek."

Pastor Danig: "It wasn't that type of kiss. It was a passionate kiss on the cheek."

She leans her lips toward his cheek and kisses him softly near his ear.

He then moves to kiss her on the lips and she blocks such a kiss with her two fingers and says, "Are you sure you want to kiss me on my lips? The lips are a point of no return!"

Pastor Danig: "I don't want to think about it!"

He then leans over and plants his lips upon hers and they both embrace in a passionate moment of kissing. He pulls back and looks over at the other guestroom, where he suggests they go. They maintain quiet so that they don't wake up the children.

Julya says, "Hold on, let me check on the children real quick."

Pastor Danig: "I'll do the same!"

They both quickly and quietly walk to the different rooms and find out that the children are still asleep. Danig gently closed the door in such a stealthy manner as if he was trained in military tactics. They both rush quietly to the guestroom and disrobe. He takes out some condoms and rolls one on his penis.

Julya: "Is this premeditated or do you normally just come out of pocket with condoms?"

Pastor Danig: "Well, we don't need any more issues. If we're going to mess up, let's not add additional drama to the scene like pregnancy or possibly disease!"

Julya: "I'm not trying to get pregnant and I have no disease. In fact, my children are the best form of birth control that money can buy!"

They begin kissing and then removing the rest of their clothing. He quickly inserts without using the condom and then thirty minutes pass and they're intimately going at it and being quiet about it but the intensity level warrants some sounds, if not screaming. At the climactic moment Danig tries to remove his penis to no avail. He is stuck inside of her and is trying to remove it. In their worries, they whisper at each other as if the whispering is going to keep things hush.

Pastor Danig: "I knew I should have not sinned like this! I cannot believe this is happening! He yells out, "God, please forgive me!" He then tries to remove it again and it seems like there was no hope is sight.

Julya: "Calm down! I've heard of something like this happening and you just need to relax! If you calm down in all areas maybe you'll get out and the sooner you calm down, the sooner we can get you out of here!"

Pastor Danig: "You're making jokes at a time like this? This is not good and the kids will be getting up soon!"

Julya: "We can't go out there stuck together with a house full of kids. They're going to wake up soon. Just calm down. If my kids wake up, I'll have them check on you kids. I'll tell them to be quiet until we're finished in here."

Pastor Danig: "This is so wrong."

Julya: "You need to calm down and stop thinking about stuff. You can pray once you get out."

Pastor Danig says with worried enthusiasm,, "I need to pray now so I can get out!"

Julya: "You're probably not going to be able to get out if you don't calm down because I'm trying to calm down and I'm the one who needs to relax. So please calm down and think of something that will cause you to calm down faster."

He pulls the covers over their connected bodies and lies there in every attempt to calm down. As they're lying there, he remains stimulated and tries to think of something that will lessen the stimulation. In his disbelief, he hears a car pull into the driveway and shortly thereafter, keys are turning the door. In his panic, he thinks that no one has as key to the house but his wife and she wasn't scheduled to arrive from her trip until the end of the week.

Maylee: "I'm home, where are you? Whose car is parked in the driveway?" She walks into the kitchen and she says, "Honey, are you in the bathroom?"

Pastor Danig: "Don't say anything! We're busted in a major way! We have a house full of kids and we're stuck together. I don't want my wife to see this!"

Julya: "It's too late for all of that, don't you think?"

In his mind, he starts to think of all the things he stood for and how he shut down people who spoke of doing wrongful things! He thought about the earlier conversation he had with the deacon. He feels like he's in a forest with no compass and there's endless trees. As the shameful moment approaches, his stimulation subsides but the connection remains.

Maylee walks in and sees them under the covers. Maylee: "Why are you sleeping in the guestroom, hun, and whose car is outside?" She doesn't realize that Julya is in the bed with him.

Pastor Danig: "That's the babysitter's car!"

Maylee: "Oh, she's here."

Pastor Danig: "Yes...."

Maylee: "Where is she?" Before he could answer Maylee approaches the bed and realizes that her husband is in the bed with another woman. In her shock, she screams and says, "w\What are you doing with another woman... ." She snatches the covers away and sees them still connected. She pauses for a moment and looks at her husband in the eye and yells hysterically, "I cannot believe what I'm seeing."

Pastor Danig: "It's not what it seems...."

Maylee: "It's not what it seems. You are having sex with another woman in the guestroom with a house full of children. You are still having sex with her even while I'm standing here!" Why are you still inside of this tramp?"

Pastor Danig: "No, it's not what it seems. We cannot get apart."

Maylee: "Oh. so you love it that much that you cannot get out! Okay, let me help you!" She runs into the other room and gets the camcorder, which is on the tripod, and sets it up in the bedroom.

Pastor Danig: "What are you doing?"

Maylee: "I need to document all evidence for my divorce proceedings."

She then runs into the kitchen and gets a huge bucket and fills it with water. She then goes into the garage and gets bags of ice and fills the bucket with ice and water. She adds salt to the water to lower the freezing point. She then stirs it up, brings the bucket to the bedroom and says, "So this is what happens when I'm away or when you're away on business! I know this isn't the first time you've been messing around and I just want you to know, Pastor Danig, I want a divorce! I now baptize you in the name of divorce."

She takes the frigid water prepared like a lab scientist and poured it slowly over their pubic region. They were both screaming.

Julya: "What the hell are you doing?"

Maylee: "You're in no position to ask me what I'm doing but since you're in my house with my husband, I'll extend my hospitality to my guests by telling you that I'm cooling down all this fire and brimstone with some cool ice water prepared in my garage lab!" As she's pouring, she exclaims, "I didn't tell you but other than making homemade ice cream, I now find use of what I learned in my college chemistry course about lowering the freezing point of water! You know, 32° Fahrenheit isn't cold enough for this situation, so I added a little saline to the soup, just enough to cool things down a bit! I don't think it would be fair to use Nitrogen, that would end it all and since I'm a proponent of grace, maybe this brew is your experience of grace and mercy!" She continues pouring the icy water onto them while they're screaming and yelling. She then goes to the phone and calls 911. Maylee: "I need an ambulance at 458 Banneker Drive in Bloomington!"

Maylee: "You're a hypocrite and I don't want anything to do with you! You and your little tramp are going to pay for this!"

She runs into the bedroom and wakes up the children while the camera is still rolling. The bed is covered with ice and water and Danig and Julya are sitting in the bed moaning and looking helpless. Pastor Danig is continuously trying to detach himself to no avail. The sounds of sirens and diesel engines could be heard screaming through the neighborhood. The ambulance and firetrucks pull up alongside the driveway. Lights are flashing and the neighbors in their curiosity are standing outside of their homes watching all of this unfold.

Pastor Danig: "What is going on and why are firetrucks outside—there's no fire."

Maylee: "THERE IS A FIRE, NIGGAH!"

Danig: "Huh…."

The paramedics enter the through the door with the fireman.

"Madam, where's the couple?"

Maylee speaks with a calm voice, "The tramp and my husband are in the other room covered in ice."

The paramedics look at each other with shock and one says, "I'm sorry, madam...."

Maylee grabs the camera and continues filming while the paramedics work on putting them both on the gurney.

They cover them up and Pastor Danig says, "Can you just give us something to fix this? I don't want to leave here like this."

Maylee: "Oh, no, you're going to leave here like this! Let everybody see the slick, secretive pastor in his indiscretion! You want to hide and act like you're perfect but I have it here on this camera. You have no decency about yourself—to bring this mess in our home in front of our children."

Pastor Danig; "You're making a spectacle...."

Maylee: "How dare you sit up here and try to talk to me while I'm sitting here witnessing you commit adultery right before my very eyes. I cannot even believe I'm having a conversation with you. Get these small-minded people out of my home. I need to call the cops. This woman is an imposter in my home and I have every right to do harm to her. She and my husband have used violence against me with what they did and I have a right to defend myself! It is mental torture and violence and the ice bath you experienced is nothing compared to the psychological mess I'm experiencing." She pauses and starts crying while speaking. "I'm leaving. I'm taking my children away from this!"

She runs in the room with the camcorder in hand and tells the children to get in the car. The neighbors are standing outside in shock as they watch the paramedics wheel the pastor and his mistress out on the gurney.

One neighbor yells, "What's going on? Is everything alright?"

The pastor looks at him from the gurney with a guilty and empty stare. Julya is holding her head down in shame. They push the gurney into the back of the unit and the paramedic starts an IV. One of the ambulance drivers takes Julya's children and tells them to ride with the fireman en route to the hospital.

As the ambulance and firetrucks leave, Maylee sits in the car with the children and begins crying. Her child asks, "What's wrong, Mom? Please don't cry."

The youngest child starts crying and the mom decides to try to hold in her cries in order to calm her younger child down. Maylee: "It's going to be alright, I'm just having some problems right now but I know God will see me through this."

Pastor Danig is en route to the hospital. He realizes that you only have but a few moments in life to make a decision about doing what's right. He thought about the deacon offering to help him and how he refused. The calling of pastor is a high calling that is not often effectively carried out by any man. He realized that his position as pastor is now jeopardized and that the thing that God called him to do won't be fulfilled in the same manner if such an event didn't happen. He is now thinking, "How in the world one can come back from such a mistake? I've committed adultery and I've hurt my wife— the one who instilled trust in me. I've allowed my fleshly desires and weakness get between the covenant I made with God and my wife. I know that all things work for good to them that love the Lord and are called according to his purpose. Lord, I believe I love you even in the midst of my wrongdoing and I know I must accept the consequence to my sin." All of these thoughts are going through his mind as they are being transported to the hospital.

Scene: Some of the members back at the church are standing around talking about the drama that has unfolded:

Girl 1: "Did you hear what happened with the pastor and the administrative assistant?"

Girl 2: "No."

Girl 1: "Yeah, he got caught cheating on his wife and a fight broke and the police were involved!"

Girl 2: "Really?"

Girl 1: "Yeah, rumor has it that she got the job through one of the deacons at the church and then she started messing around with the pastor on the side."

Girl 2: "What! That sounds crazy! I can't believe that Pastor Danig messed around on his wife! His wife is such a beautiful and nice lady! Why would he go out on her like that?"

Girl 1: "Girl, you know how these men are. They gotta have that woman on the side! It boosts their ego!"

Girl 2: "It didn't seem like he had an ego problem!"

Girl 1: "He did! Just look at the type of car he drove and he's the pastor. These men need other people to fulfill their needs. That's why pastors are pastors. They need all of the attention from other people and they must keep getting this attention from people. He was probably poking her at that conference that all these pastors go on every year!"

Girl 2: "That's crazy! I don't understand why someone who seems to have so many good things happening for them would actually go out on their marriage. It makes me sick and I'm tired of hearing stories like this. I don't even want to go to church anymore and look at this fool in the face. All this time, he was preaching the word like he was some anointed person. He helped me get out of a sinful situation by the way he preached. He always preached about sin and how we should show God how much we love Him by keeping his commandments."

Girl 1: "Well, no one said the man was perfect. I think he tried to do this job which has so much pressure and so many expectations. I think people expect men or women of God to be more than human and that really isn't possible. I applaud him for the good things he's done but I don't think any man is above reproach. It just looks so bad when it's coming from a minister. These guys shouldn't get up there and act all holy if that can't handle the calling because now I'm ready to leave the church."

Girl 2: "Are you kidding? You're ready to leave the church because of the wrongdoing of a man? That doesn't make any sense!"

Girl 1: "It makes sense to me. I don't want to support a ministry or person who's the head of that ministry if they can't live right before the people they are leading. I believe we need to live by example. I have enough sense to know that we're all weak but what about all the other members who see this type of thing going on. They won't get delivered and the problems that people are struggling with will continue because the leaders aren't showing how much God has made the difference in their lives. I really don't get it." There are people out there who aren't even going to church and they're being loyal to their mates."

Girl 2: "That doesn't mean that they're going to heaven, though."

Girl 1: "But the fact remains, they aren't out there hypocrite on the word of God. Didn't the Bible say that he would hold people accountable who mislead the flock? It said something like that and he is going to pay for his wrongdoing. I want to go to a place where there isn't so much drama and the men of God are real. I want to be in the community of people who really want to live right and who are making the word something real in their lives. I want to be in that place where people aren't phony and there's a sense of genuine service to people and God. These people over here are players and they're just out for the money. I don't understand how someone can just sleep with someone outside of their marriage."

Girl 2: "This ain't nuthin' new. Do you honestly think that sin occurs outside of the church? Girl, you need to realize that people are messed up."

Girl 1: "You're getting on my nerves. I can't believe you're trying to stand up for this pastor."

Girl 2: "I'm not standing up for this pastor. I'm just telling it like it is. He made a mistake and he is going to have to pay for that mistake. I'm not going to apologize for the people who fail to see that he is just a man that is of the flesh, which wants to do wrong all the time. Even those who do admit that they have sinful thoughts and ways, the fact remains, you can't trust the flesh. You need to put your full trust in God and stop acting like your whole world is turned upside down because some man made a mistake."

Girl 1: "You of all people want to sit up here and talk about a man making a mistake when your man did the same thing to you. You want to act super holy because you see another person making the same mistake your ex-husband made on you."

Girl 2: "Look at the consequence of those mistakes. We aren't together anymore and the kids had to grow up in a single home. I didn't ask for those problems but they happened."

Girl 1: "Well, I think we understand that people that think the way you do continue to follow people who keep on making mistakes. I don't need to be in some church where people are constantly making mistakes and misleading people. I think people who fail to wake up and see this type of wrongdoing are simply brainwashed. They want to continue following somebody because that person in no different than they are. As cynical as it sounds, I think people enjoy it when they see someone fall. This pastor seemed like he had everything and now he is going to be shut down. His role in this church will be something less than what he's doing now because he couldn't handle the role of superhuman."

The End

— The character of a pimp… —

The pastor has been raising money for years for the building fund and there's no building in sight or the existing building is in disrepair. The same pastor is riding around in a Rolls Royce and the building is in need of a paint job. The bathrooms are in desperate need of repair or upgrade. The church is in need of new carpet that has been worn out through weekly dancing and shouting. In addition, the average household income in the community is $20,000; 30% of the congregation is on some type of public assistance; and the community suffers from gang violence, drugs, and dilapidated schools.

— The preacher raises money to advance his cause —uses money to buy a dream house. —

The pastor comes to church in moderate apparel and a mediocre vehicle to distract the members but when you follow him home, there's a 10,000-square-foot mansion, a Lamborghini, and a couple of BMWs in the driveway in some house on the hill and the reason for obtaining these items was not through some incredible successful investment in the stock market or some boom in a home-based business—rather it was the money that was successfully raised in the church.

— The preacher uses his pulpit power to advance on susceptible women. —

In the society that we live in, there are women who will put themselves in the midst of a person who has power—the power to speak before crowds, the power to raise money, the power to win people over and the power to manipulate the minds of people via the use of innuendoes in the pulpit. The Bible does say that life and death are given in the power of the tongue and many of these pastors know the word. They've studied the word—they've studied veteran preachers who've successfully pastor mega ministries. They followed their parents who might have been pastors who might have dragged them to church on Sundays and days throughout the week. They've now taken it to another level—perhaps another dimension.

Having knowledge of someone's downfall is the opportunity for pastors to imbed such problems into their sermons. It is amazing that the confidentiality clause no longer applies as some pastors feel that if they don't use the person's name in the sermon, that they've accomplished the confidentiality clause. Everyone knows that this is not the case when dealing with some ministers. They will have someone in their office and they will vow that such information will be kept in confidence and then the sermon will have someone's business as part of the expository text. The sad notion, however, is that although names might not be used, the person that is being made an example of knows they're the ones being spoken of and the people in their circles know that the pastor is preaching about them. The interesting thing though is that many of the problems that are confessed in pastor's office are problems that many people might have and so when the pastor preaches about them, it is applicable to many people. Perhaps the mindset is to help people who have similar problems but some get hurt in the process. Some are embarrassed to the point of sometimes leaving the ministry.

— The preacher works the emotions of the crowd to purge money for his vision. —

Now if a pastor told you that God told him something and prophesied that if you did not obey the word of the profit, then you'd be like the person on some game show who vacillated on some decision continue with hopes of winning more money or remaining and taking a smaller amount of money. You want to obey the prophet and so shall you prosper life the Bible says. Now the questions remain. How do I know if I'm obeying a true prophet of God? How do I know if this person not some impostor who is acting in the name of the Lord? The Bible does say that the very elect can be fooled.

There are people who go about in the name of the Lord simply to manipulate and then there are those who simply cannot handle the power when the make it to some plateau in the ministry. The ones who intentionally do wrong to manipulate people should be jailed. The ones who follow in the footsteps of those who came before them need to be fined and counseled.

━ The pastor allows members to deify him without notifying those in need that he suffers from the same affliction. ━

Those who attend a Christian church realize that the focus is on Christ and man is only a vessel that will hear from God if he attempts to live a life that is Godly. Well, if the pastor is living a life that is Godly and the members look to him for counsel over issues that the pastor himself might suffer from—then how is it possible for one to counsel another if they are currently going through the same problem? How can one give advice on a sensitive issue of lusting over another woman if he is currently lusting? Some might justify the notion that none of us are really good enough to get on a platform to advise on things that afflicts us but at least one who might have that we are all of the flesh and nothing good dwells in the flesh.

━ The pastor dissuades other members from pimping. ━

As a means to not allow another potential pimp from cutting in on the business, the pimp will use the necessary tactics to prevent others from getting into the pimping business. It is interesting to note the insidious nature of how pimps work. If a member in the ministry was interested in starting a ministry within the church and noted that the members were gravitating towards this ministry, he might become jealous. He/she will do things to prevent such a ministry from taking off if that ministry jeopardizes or pulls away the attention from the initial ministry. It might be difficult to assert that this is a form of pimping since it might look like some church member simply has a take-over spirit. Members do walk around saying, "Yeah, he just has a takeover spirit." They just want to steal members and eventually start their own church. Now events like this do actually take place. Pastors have been in conflict with members who decided to form ministries within a ministry. If the pastor does not support it, then they will eventually move on to start their own ministry. They might even go as far as downgrading or talking negative against the existing ministry. When the finally leave the ministry, they will steal some of the members. Now this does sound ridiculous. Stealing members? Since when did a ministry have ownership of members? Yes, the grant money and loans that banks give might have in its clause that in order for you to get the loan or get approved for the money, you need to have a certain amount of members. We need to see growth in the ministry of a period of time. Now if the vision of the pastor is to build a large edifice, which involves purchasing land, etc., then membership becomes an important factor.

The church is a business and it is run like a business. People in the church are humans that have their likes and dislikes. The church has clicks and people in the church are materialistic.

Materialism is something that cannot be overlooked. Some ministries will use materialism and a guide to you being blessed or not. If you are without, then you are cursed. If you have material gain, then you are blessed. That is one of the criteria. The other criterion to being blessed is having good health. If your health is compromised, then you are not blessed. This is the message that essentially comes out of the pulpits. Members who are blessed are following the principal of tithing and if you don't tithe, then you will be cursed with a cursed. Will a man rob God is commonly uttered from the pulpit. One should bring their first fruits and tithe in a manner that will get you blessed. You will be blessed financially because tithing in the church focuses on the financial picture rather that giving 10 percent of service. But service can have a monetary component to it as well.

━ The pastor is an isogetical expert. ━

The pastor uses the scriptures and sermons only for the benefit of getting a response from the crowd. After years of churching and studying scriptures, sociology and the like, many pastors know the art of what to say to the people. Let's be real, people in the church are there with issues and are in need of some type of spiritual and tangible intervention.

The things that are very clear in life are some of the things that pastors focus on while preparing these pimped out sermons. There are things that are very clear in life and that that can be summarized in the following issues:

- Finances
- Relationships
- Health

◄ The modern-day use of the term "pimp" as it relates to the pimping of the church edifice: ◄

The process of doing church has a physical place of worship. The institution itself is housed in a monumental place of sorts—a place that has ecumenical and breathtaking impacts as in some cathedrals. One might consider that a place where the worship of God takes place should not be anything less than a place of greatness. Others might disagree that since God is omnipresent and since everything belongs to God, the place should not matter. While considering the two, the former argument has the impact of placing so much attention on worldly things while giving spiritual things less attention. While we have the wherewithal to do something for God, why not build something that shows the intent that what we do for God has to have a greater impact than what we do for the world. The church edifice should be more spectacular than a stadium devoted to sports, concerts, and the like that places attention on man. While considering the latter, it should not matter as God owns everything and he's looking at the heart. God does not need a physical representation from man to establish true worship. God is looking at the heart. A place where one worships God should not be less than a place of greatness. It must have the stature and the power that the notion of praising God demands. It must be a place of safety and a place where time and consideration was placed into putting the edifice and the alter together. The subtext of this continues to permeate the minds of pastors who've studied scripture and who have tried to follow in the footsteps of former architects for the building of Churches.

The modern day of pimping the church building is now an issue for many churches. Some church leaders take a more conservative role when designing the church building while others will take pimping to an ostentatious level. You'll note that some churches have to adorn pillars with gold plating to emulate expensive metals used to make the structure. Perhaps the mindset is that church deserves the best that architect can offer and the look is important, too. Well, it is outrageous to think that the worship of God needs physical attributes such as a fancy building to enable worship. It is akin to a graven image. It is a shame to think that a fancy building with all of the accoutrements is necessary to facilitate worship. Some members have the notion that that will not do church unless it is in a place that has the sophistication that builds upon pride. Pride is something spoken negatively of in the scriptures but it seems to take precedence here. The churchgoer is more apt to invite someone to their ministry when things seem ecumenical and the place of worship is a much talked about facility. The notion is that many of the modern-day ministries have built fancy structures to house thousands of members in a sanctuary that has taken on a modern approach. The use of PowerPoint-type presentations during praise and worship, the use of WIFI in the church to enable members with laptops and/or pocket PCs to get the sermon or their Bibles online while listening to the sermon, the use of modern instruments—sequencers, horn arrangements, full band—encompassing a big-band dynamic, the use of violins, etc.—to enhance the music ministry. In the past, some of the richer churches such as the Catholic Church were able to build sanctuaries whereby the architecture was in the millions of dollars. Inside such structures could be found expensive pipe organs that ranged in the millions of dollars and the maintenance of such musical instrument demanded hundreds of thousands of dollars annually. While considering how technology has enabled modern-day ministries to economize by using keyboard music workstations that can emulate the sounds of pipe organs, pianos, organs, etc., the price to build the structure has now become a reasonable thing. The price to put together a church that houses five to ten thousand people can now efficiently take place with a little efficiency and the use of calculus in maximizing profits while minimizing costs.

➤ A message to the pimps in the church: ➤

If you realize that you are pimp and have no intention of changing, then it is apparent that you don't believe in the divine creator nor do you believe in the consequences of doing wrong against your fellow man. However, feel free to read because you might have a change of heart.

➤ Follow these steps if you are a pimp in ministry and seek redemption: ➤

Step 1. Ask the divine creator to forgive you for the pimping you have done and sincerely be sorry for this wrongdoing. Do not simply be sorry because your wrongdoing is exposed and you feel it is politically correct to do so. Do not apologize with the mindset that they will forgive you while you wait for the smoke to clear so you can continue pimping.

Step 2. Stand before your congregation and all of the people that you have pimped and simply apologize. While you are apologizing, be specific about what you are apologizing about and do not make excuses for the wrong that you have done.

Step 3. If you had a worldwide ministry and you solicited money via telephone, Internet, television, radio and other media forms, be prepared to return this money—all of it, not a portion of it. In fact, for those who have been pimping for decades, return it to today's value (include inflation and the cost of living).

Step 4. Sell everything that you obtained with other people's money and return the money to the people in need. This includes the house or mansion that you purchased, the Maybach or similar luxury vehicle, the jet that you've purchased or are leasing.

Step 5. Calculate the moneys spent on international trips such as to Africa, Europe and the Middle East for so-called missionary work that ended up being a vacation and return this amount to the same fund that should be used to help the poor.

Step 6. Write a book or create a blog on how you scammed people out of money and how you were delivered from such a lifestyle and use all proceeds from the sale of your book to help poverty in the town where you are domiciled. Your book should warn pimps that are continuing in this behavior.

Step 7. Go to Bible colleges and universities and seminary schools as a guest speaker and warn the newbies of the pimps out there and give them incite on how to not become a pimp.

Step 8. Admit to the congregation that you didn't really believe in what you were preaching about. Be specific. Tell them that you did not believe that Christ died on a cross for sins and that none of the commandments meant anything to you. Indicate that if it actually meant something to you, you might have tried to follow the principles in the Bible. Let them know that you realized the benefit in being the pimp of a nonprofit organization and that the benefits of a 501c3 corporation was too good to pass up. Express your real feelings on the matter and help people realize that they were pimped.

Step 9. If you continue to get money from the membership on a weekly basis, treat them like investors who buy stock in the company. When the ministry profits in its nonprofit status, give the members an opportunity to "put"!